Photograph by International
ENTERPRISE
Racing Marvel, Harold S. Vanderbilt, Skipper, successful defender of *America's* Cup, against Sir Thomas Lipton's *Shamrock V*

THE BOOK OF MARVELS

By
HENRY SMITH WILLIAMS, M.D., LL.D.
Author of
"The Story of Modern Science"
"The Great Astronomers"
"The Biography of Mother Earth", etc.

FUNK & WAGNALLS COMPANY
NEW YORK AND LONDON

TRI-MOTOR TWELVE-PASSENGER FOKKER CABIN PLANE OF WESTERN AIR EXPRESS, WITH MT. SAN JACINTO, CAL., IN BACKGROUND. THIS IS THE REGULAR ROUTE FOR PLANE FROM KANSAS CITY TO LOS ANGELES

Copyright, 1931, by
FUNK & WAGNALLS COMPANY
[Printed in the United States of America]

Copyright Under the Articles of the Copyright Convention of the
Pan-American Republics and the United States.

INTRODUCTION

WE often hear it said that the age of miracles is past. This is an obvious mistake. We have but to look about us to realize that the greatest age of miracles is just beginning. Anyone who is familiar with the history of scientific progress in the past third of a century can cite offhand at least a score of achievements that are nothing less than miraculous.

Here is such an offhand list, each item representing the attainment of what might well have been considered the impossible:

(1) The discovery of the X-ray, enabling us to see through such opaque things as the human body.

(2) The discovery of the electron, unit structure of both electricity and matter, giving us a glimpse into the structure of the atom.

(3) The discovery of radium and the allied minerals, making possible the old dreams of the alchemist.

(4) The measurement and actual counting of atoms so small that billions of them could reside on the point of a needle—like the hypothetical angels of medieval speculation.

(5) The observation with the ultramicroscope of particles of matter thousands of times smaller than even the microscope could hitherto reveal.

(6) The finding of four new gases in the air, including helium, which had previously been discovered in the sun with the aid of the spectroscope.

(7) The development of serum therapy, through which, for example, diphtheria is conquered with a serum developed in the body of a horse.

(8) The development of vaccine therapy, whereby typhoid fever and other plagues are prevented.

(9) Making the Panama Canal Zone and similar pest-ridden places salubrious, through the discovery that mosquitoes are the sole carriers of germs of malaria and yellow fever.

(10) Making a boat that can dive under water and swim there like a fish.

(11) Making an automobile, driven by whiffs of exploding gas, that can go several miles a minute.

(12) Making an airplane, weighing a ton or more, that can rise into the air in defiance of gravitation and fly at a speed of two or three miles per minute, long enough to cross the ocean.

(13) Making a balloon of enormous size that can be driven into the wind and guided on transcontinental and transoceanic voyages.

(14) Sending telegraph signals across the ocean by wireless.

(15) Talking half way around the world by radio.

(16) Taking nitrogen from the air, with the aid of electricity, to make destructive explosives on one hand and constructive soil for fertilizers on the other.

(17) Making many-hued dyes and useful chemicals from coal tar.

(18) Photographing myriads of stars lying infinitely beyond the range of human vision.

(19) Measuring a star so distant that its light requires some years to come to us, though traveling at a speed of 186,000 miles per second.

(20) Testing and measuring the speed of light with laboratory apparatus.

Each and every one of these achievements is necromantic. Most of them would have subjected the discoverers to danger of prosecution for witchcraft in an earlier age. Now we understand that no natural law is violated—although sometimes man's preconceptions, based on unwarranted assumptions, are rudely shattered. That, in effect, is the province of any miracle.

In scanning such a list, one's mind reverts naturally to the allied "miracles" of an elder day. In particular, one thinks of the famed seven wonders of antiquity. Most readers will recall, perhaps, that the Pyramids of Egypt, the Hanging Gardens of Babylon, the Temple of Diana at Ephesus, and the Colossus of Rhodes were among them. The others were the Pharos of Alexandria—a lighthouse about 400 feet high—the Statue of Jupiter by Phidias in the Parthenon at Athens, and the Mausoleum of Artemisia. All these so-called wonders, then, were examples of engineering or architectural skill or of sculpture on a colossal scale.

In our day gigantic engineering and architectural enterprises have become so common that their results have for the most part ceased to cause wonder. In other directions, however, as we have just seen, the scientific workers of our time have produced results that excite the astonishment even of the initiated.

A few years ago the publishers of *Popular Mechanics* sought to ascertain which among modern achievements are best entitled, in the opinion of experts, to rank as the seven most remarkable of present-day wonders. They made out a list including fifty-six discoveries or inventions of modern times, all of which might properly be described as wonderful. The list was comprehensive in its scope, including the results of great engineering efforts such as the Simplon Tunnel, the Catskill Aque-

INTRODUCTION

duct, Subway Transportation, and the Panama Canal at one end of the scale, and such achievements of theoretical science as have to do with ultra-violet rays, the ultra-microscope, and synthetic chemistry at the other.

This comprehensive list of modern achievements was sent out to one thousand eminent men in Europe and America, including members of the French Academy of Science, the Royal Society of London, the great German Universities, and the American Academy of Science. The request was made that each would mark off on the list of fifty-six subjects the seven that seemed to him to represent the most wonderful modern achievements. It is reported that about seven hundred of the scientists responded. The result of their balloting is not definite, of course, but it has obvious interest. It presents seven modern "wonders," in the following order: (1) the wireless telegraph; (2) the telephone; (3) the airplane; (4) radium; (5) antiseptics and antitoxins; (6) spectrum analysis; (7) the X-ray.

We are told that only a single voter checked each of these seven "wonders" on his list, this being Dr. Theodore Paul, of the Royal University of Munich. Six ballots, one from India, two from France, two from Germany, and one from the United States, showed the selection of six of the final seven. As further illustrating the wide diversity of opinion, it is to be noted that, although the wireless telegraph led all competing wonders by a wide margin, the vote for it was only 244, or just over one-third of the total. Meantime the telephone, second on the list, received only 185 votes, or a little over one-fourth of the total. The airplane received 167 votes, and the others successively fewer down to the X-ray with 111 votes. The three next most popular wonders, making up a total list of ten, were in succession, the Panama Canal, anesthesia, and synthetic chemistry. The last named of these may fairly be considered too vague and general a subject to be rightly listed with the other specific achievements.

In our present BOOK OF MARVELS, the miraculous achievements just listed, and many others of only less vital significance, receive attention as a matter of course. But we have occasion also to introduce some scores of "marvels" which, at first glance, may seem in no wise comparable, but which on reflection will be seen to be entitled to legitimate rank among the wonders of civilization. The steam engine of Watt, for example; or the locomotive of Trevithick. We might even go farther back in time, and name the first implement of chipped stone, the first bow and arrow, the first potter's wheel, and a half-score other prehistoric inventions, among the greatest accomplishments of the human intellect. If we omit some of these, it is only because they are so universally familiar that it seemed best to give the space they would claim to more novel exhibits.

This statement in itself implies a certain latitude in the interpretation of the meaning of the word "marvel." In particular it suggests that the element of novelty enters into the case. Let it be said explicitly that many inventions or phenomena are admitted as "marvels" that are seemingly wonderful chiefly because they are unfamiliar; and that many phenomena intrinsically far more wonderful are given scant attention because they are matters of every-day observation. Take the case of gravity, for example. There is no phenomenon in all nature more inexplicable than the fall of a pencil that you release from your hand. Yet it would seem farcical to depict this incident on a par with, let us say, the flight of an airplane—though the latter is far less mysterious.

One might continue indefinitely such an analysis of the meaning of the word "marvel," in explication of this or that inclusion or exclusion of phenomena or accomplishments more or less obviously "wonderful." Such an analysis, however, could not be other than boresome. Let the reader who is interested in speculations of this character make such an analysis for himself, and he will perhaps be disposed, occasionally at least, to modify an incipient criticism as to the inclusion of here and there a "marvel" that to him does not seem intrinsically wonderful, or the exclusion of something that he regards as truly marvelous.

As auxiliary to such critical analysis, many readers will find interest, I am sure, in raising and for themselves answering—or attempting to answer—the very natural, but difficult, question as to which is the one greatest marvel of all among the hosts of unchallengeable "wonders" presented in THE BOOK OF MARVELS.

A word about the pictures. Nearly all were furnished by Brown Brothers, of New York City, who have supplied photographic material for many of my earlier books, and whose helpful cooperation I highly appreciate.

H. S. W.

THE SKY-LINE OF LOWER NEW YORK, PHOTOGRAPHED FROM THE BROOKLYN BRIDGE

INDEXED CONTENTS

Agassiz Column, Yosemite Valley, California, 103
Air, gripping the, 39
Airplane, Fokker, 2; the first airplane, 18; early Wright model in France, 18; how it grips the air, 39; London to Tokyo in four days, 112; historic flights, 128
Airplane carrier, latest type of, 58
Airplanes, bomb-dropping, 59
Airship, new type of, 23
Akron, airship, pictured and described, 9
Allanosaur, carnivorous, 35
Alligator, hatching an, 97
Amber, fly in the, 35
Amonton, Guillaume, pioneer inventor of steam engine, 19
Amundsen, Captain Roald, at the South Pole, 42
Animals, comparative intelligence of, 56
Antitoxin, obtaining from a horse, 69
Anti-typhoid vaccine, 28
Apple, Baldwin, creator of, 98
Aqueduct, a modern, in Los Angeles, 54
Arizona, American battleship, 59
Arkwright, Richard, inventor, 44
Arlington, radio time signals from, 20
Armadillo, the strangest animal in America, 114
Arrowrock Dam, Boise, Idaho, 72
Artist, feathered, 117
Asbestos suits, to protect firemen, 11
Assyria, sculptures from, 62
Astronomical instruments, ancient Chinese, 31
Astronomy, making a hobby of, 70
Atoms, the counting of, 125
Automobile, chimneys for, 48; earliest and latest passenger models, 48; an amphibious, 79

Ball, hitting the, 16
Ballooning, a new era in, 38
Balloons, early scientific superstitions regarding, 118
Barbot, George, pioneer glider, 18
Barnes, C. E., on how to build a telescope, 91
Bat, picture of, 115
Battleship, latest type of, 58, 59; seventeenth-century type, 119
Bauman, John E., his experiments with chimpanzees, 94
Bear, on skates, 56
Bear Mountain Bridge, 123
Beaver, tender of submarine, 78
Bees, the first radio users, 83
Bell, Dr. Alexander Graham, inventor of the telephone, 24, 25
Benzene ring, an important element of protoplasm, 21
Berquen, Ludwig van, pioneer diamond polisher, 101
Bicycle, early type of, 49
Biddle, Dr. Oscar, 78
Bird, the thriftiest, 77
Birds, mystery of their migration, 57
Blimp, first in New York, 38
Blind, the, teaching to read type by ear, 20, 21
Blood corpuscles, counting with the microscope, 21
Blood pressure, tests for, 89
Boats, flying, 38
Boiling a kettle on ice, 14
Boll weevil, methods of combating, 23
Bombing the boll weevil, 23
Bothner, George, and his famous "scissors-hold," 16
Brahe, Tycho, his quadrant, 90
Branca, Giovanni, pioneer inventor of steam engine, 19

Bremen, swift German liner, 99
Bridge, Natural, at Zion Park, 32; Buffalo-Fort Erie Peace, 122; Quebec, 122; International, at Niagara, 122; the Sault Ste. Marie, 123; Bear Mountain, 123
Bridges, some marvelous, 25
Brontosaurs, a painting of, 34
Burbank, Luther, work of, 36; creator of the Shasta daisy, 76; creator of the spineless cactus, 77
Byrd, Admiral, flight of over the North Pole, 43; his reception in New York, 43

Cactus, spineless, how developed, 77
Cactus plants, reservoirs of water, 37
Call-bell, inventor of, 122
Camouflage, nature's use of, 96
Candles, still used in the twentieth century, 101
Caterpillar, tent, 36
Cellulose, how made into paper, 25
Charlotte Dundas, pioneer stern-wheel steamer, 98
Chart of famous flights, 128
Chemical elements, patrician and plebeian, 81
Chemistry, use of the microscope in, 100
Chimpanzee, learning to sew, 56; inoculating a, 88; remarkable strength of, 94
Chipmunks, 75
Chromosomes, important function of, 115
Chrysler Building, New York, 103
Cleopatra's Needle, Central Park, New York, 63
Clermont, Fulton's first steamship, 98, 99
Cleveland, Ohio, unique sanitarium in, 12
Cliff-dwellers of Arizona, 102; of Colorado, 103
Cliff Palace, Mesa Verde National Park, 61
Clock, astronomical, at U. S. Naval Observatory, 20
Clocks that must be coddled, 20
Clouds and rain, 41
Clouds over the Dolomites, 41
Cold-heat paradox, 62
Cold light, how created, 20
Cole, Prof. Leon J., on poultry breeding, 17
Colorado River, harnessing the, 12
Coloration, protective, nature's use of, 96
Color-blindness, inheritance of, 30
Colosseum, rim of the Roman, 17
Comet, Brooks's, 50; a celestial ghost, 50; a celestial vagabond, 50
Condor, the champion glider, 13
Congo, fashions in the, 11
Coolidge Dam, Arizona, 37
Corona, seen during an eclipse, 31
Cotton gin, invention of, 44
Cowbird, invader of other birds' nests, 117
Crater Lake, one of the wonders of Oregon, 113
Crew, F. A. E., 78
Cruisers, modern types of, 58
Cuckoo, European, strange habits of, 117
Cugnot, French inventor of first self-propelled vehicle, 48
Current motor, or tide machine, 105

Dalton, John, early instance of color-blindness, 30
Daly, Dr. Richard R., 88
Dam, Hoover, site of, 12
Daniel, John, famous gorilla, 94
Date Line, International, 128
Deer, surgical experiment upon, 88
DeForest, Lee, inventor of radio tubes, 86

5

INDEXED CONTENTS

Deforestation, disastrous effects of, 33
Devil fish, terror of the diver, 14
Diamonds, how they are polished, 101
Dinosaurs, eggs of, 34; largest carnivorous beasts, 34
Diphtheria, latest methods of treating, 69
Diplodocus, a prehistoric monster, 54
Dirigible, the *Akron,* view of, 9; first in New York, 38; invention of, 39; historic flights by, 128
Diver, dreaded foe of, 14; at work on a wreck, 27; deep-sea at work, 79
Diving for treasure, 17
Dolmens, in Brittany and at Stonehenge, 63
Dolomites, view of, 53
DO-X, German flying boat, 38
Drowning, apparatus to rescue from, 119
Drum-head lips; the fashion in the Congo, 11
Dynamo, the mysterious, 40; evolution of the, 41
Dynamos, water-driven, 41

Eagle, bald, robbing a fish-hawk, 16
Earthquakes, causes of, 10; effects of in Yokohama, 10
Echoes from the sea bottom, 125
Edison phonograph, pioneer form of, 24
Eel, strange life history of, 74
Eel grass, raising a crop of, 35
Eggs, manufacture of in a laboratory, 124
Eggs 300,000,000 years old, 34
Egypt, temples of, 63
Ehrlich, Doctor, discoveries of, 29
Eiffel Tower, Paris, 82
Electric light, 40
Electric power, transmission of, 60
Electrical machine that does the work of five million men, 15
Electricity, use of for milking, 125
Electromagnetic waves, action of, 86
Elephant, strange use for, 56
Emmet, Dr. William LeRoy, inventor of mercury-vapor engine, 121
Empire State Building, New York, 118
Engine, steam, evolution of, 19; the turbine, 80; type invented by Parsons, 80; internal-combustion, 104; mercury-vapor, 121
Enterprise, a sailing marvel, 1
Ether, where first administered, 69
Ether waves made visible, 43
Exercise, what it is, 16

Fakirs, Hindu, how they walk through fire, 11
Faraday, Michael, greatest of experimental physicists, 15
Fear, why teach to children? 114
Fire, ordeal by, 9; walking through, 11
Fish, how to drown a, 12; how the world looks to a, 53
Fitch, John, steamboat inventor, 98
Flamingoes, a colony of, 94
Fleas, methods of fighting, 109
Flight, swiftest on record, 17
Flights, famous, chart of, 128
Flour, as an explosive, 46
Fly, fruit, experiments with, 76, 115; enemy of mankind, 108; in the amber, 35
Fokker airplane, 2
Ford, Henry, how he solved one of his problems, 24
Forest, killed by girdling trees, 112
Frog, strange development from tadpole, 19
Fruit flies, experiments with, 76, 115
Fungus, destructive parasite, 37

Games, popularity of, 17
Gar Wood and his power boat, 26
Gas engine, early types of, 104; how it works, 104
Gasoline, manufacture of, 64
Gatty and Post, world flight of, 11
General Electric Company, 21

Geyser, Oblong, crater of, 53; Old Faithful, 93; last throes of a, 112
Ghosts, celestial, 50
Giants, eight-foot, 9
Gilbert, William, discoverer of magnetic pole, 86
Glacier Point, in Yosemite Park, 52
Glaciers, how they work, 93
Glider, Farman, getting into the air, 13
Gliding, a popular sport, 13
Goiter, causes of, 29
Gorgas, General William C., work of, 42
Graf Zeppelin, the, 39
Grand Canyon of the Yellowstone, 24; of the Colorado, 92
Grand View Trail, Grand Canyon of the Colorado, 92
Gravitation, the most mysterious thing in the world, 15
Gray, Elisha, American inventor of the telephone, 24
Gun, automatic, new type of, 65
Gyroscope, stabilizing effects of, 126; use of to guide airplanes without living pilots, 127

Half Dome, Yosemite Valley, 92
Harrowing, 85
Harvester, the modern, 84
Hay fever, causes of, 45
Heart action, how to test, 89
Helicopter, principle of the, 23
Heliotropism, experiments in, 76
Helium gas, use of in dirigibles, 38, 80
Hen, mechanical, 124
Henry, Joseph, pioneer in electromagnetism, 122
Heredity, before and after Mendel, 103
Hermit Trail, Grand Canyon National Park, 92
Hog cholera, inoculating against, 88
Hole, how to bore a square, 123
Hoover Dam, Colorado River, 12
Horizon, artificial, for the navigator, 111
Horse, why he is passing, 84
Horses, a team of thirty, 124
House fly, human enemy, 108
Hurricane, effects of at sea, 118
Hydroelectric plant, Caribou, California, 105

Ice, use of to boil a kettle, 14
Icebergs, terror of mariners, 33
Ice-breaker, used by Admiral Byrd, 43
Ingenuity versus muscle, 41
Intelligence tests, 23
Invalides, Hotel des, tomb of Napoleon, 83
Invisible, seeing the, 43
Iodin, our need of, 28
Ironclads, first types of, 59
Irrigating with ice, 64
Irrigation ditches, digging in the desert, 84; in Oregon and Washington, 116
Ivory, fossil, in Alaska, 55; shipment of African, 55

Journalism, up to date, in the sky, 87
Jupiter, striped jacket of, 90

Kay Don and his power boat, 26
Kekule's ring, the unit construction of all organic compounds, 21
Kelp, harvesting for potash, 35
Kempton, J. H., his studies in heredity, 103
Klemperer, making his record flight, 13
Knife with ninety-two blades, 101
Korn, Dr. Arthur, inventor of method of sending pictures by radio, 26

Lace-making, mysteries of, 44
Lake, a man-made, 93
Lamps, a thousand in one, 21
Langley, United States airplane carrier, 58
Lava needles, in Yellowstone Park, 51

INDEXED CONTENTS

Leavitt, Miss, expert on star clusters, 90
Lester, Dr. H. H., his radiographic method, 28
Lever, principle of the, 41
Lexington, American airplane carrier, 58
Life, testing the fire of, 89
Life-preserver, a new kind of, 113
Life-saving mechanism, a new, 10
Light, speed of, 14; cold, how produced, 20; essential to life, 68; how to produce without heat, 84
Lightning, artificial, 100
Light year, definition of, 14
Lindbergh, Colonel Charles A., famous solo flight of, 22; flight to Japan, 22
Linotype, the modern type-setter, 124
Lion cub, training a, 56
Lobster, strange ways of, 113
Locomotive, an air-propelled, 14; early and late models of, 46; electric, in tug-of-war with steamer, 60; largest modern type of, 66
Loganberry, origin of, 36
London to Tokyo in four days, 112
Los Angeles, firemen of, wearing asbestos suits, 11; turbo-generator at, 15; aqueduct at, 54

Magnet, testing a big, 86; lifting car-wheels by, 87
Mammoths, remains of, found in Alaska, 55
Man, Neanderthal, 74; oldest known type of, 74
Map-making, from the sky, 82
Marble, mountains of, 53
Mariners, peril of, from icebergs, 33
Marlborough, Britain's great battleship, 58
Mars, possible inhabitants of, 30; canals of, 30; supposed ice-cap of, 30; life in, 90
Matches, the manufacture of, 106
Maya civilization, wonders of, 102
Meat diet, connection of with genius, 109
Meteor, in the earth's atmosphere, 110
Metric system, advantages of, 57
Metropolitan Life Building, 40
Miami, Florida, speedboats at, 26
Microphone, an early type of, 24
Microscope, the compound, 21; used in modern chemistry, 100
Migration mysteries, 116
Milk, the Pasteurization of, 68; vitamins in, 68
Milking by electricity, 125
Minds that cease developing, 23
Miners, safeguarding, 122
Mirror, an extraordinary natural, 112
Monitor, in battle with *Merrimac,* 59
Monolith, giant, in Red Canyons Park, 72
Monster, a three-horned, 54
Montana, geological history in, 75
Monuments that live and grow, 98
Moon, how it got its pockmarks, 70
Moore, Major Edward T., inventor of electric sling, 107
Morgan, Prof. Thomas Hunt, 76
Morning Eagle Falls, Glacier National Park, Montana, 112
Morning Glory Spring, Yellowstone Park, 72
Morse, Samuel F. B., inventor of telegraphy, 120
Morton, Dr. William, administering ether, 69
Mother of worlds, the nebula, 10
Motorcycle, curious type of, 46
Mound Terrace, Yellowstone Park, 73
Mountain, tearing down a, 33; typical, in Utah, 53
Mountain climbers will have their fun, 17
Muscles, human, how they work, 16
Mystery, the greatest in the world, 15

Napoleon, tomb of, 83
Naval Radio Station, Arlington, Virginia, 20
Nebula, spiral, 10; ring, 70, 71; owl, 71
Newton, Sir Isaac, inventor of the refracting telescope, 30

Niagara Falls, a great generator at, 15; in winter, 32; colossal power plant at, 100
Nitrogen, extraction of from air, 60
North Pole, Byrd's flight over, 43; as a way station, 52
Notre Dame, Cathedral of, Paris, 83
"Novelty," pioneer locomotive, 47

Ocean, farming the, 35
Octopus, dreaded foe of the diver, 14
Oil, for troubled waters, 93
Oil forest, typical modern, 65
Oil industry, amazing development of, 64
Oil well, the first, 64; in Texas, 65
Opossum, picture of, 114
Orange, navel, origin of, 36
Ordeal by fire, 9
Oriole, Baltimore, wonderful weaver, 117

Panama Canal, facts about, 81
Paper, how made from trees, 25
Paris, seen from an airplane, 82
Parsec, definition of, 14
Parthenon, temple of ancient Greeks, 62
Pasteur Institute, recent work of, 88
Pear, Seckel, named for its creator, 98; Bartlett, 98
Peary, Admiral, at the North Pole, 42
Penguin, one of the strangest of birds, 102
Phenomenal berry, Burbank's invention, 36
Phonograph, Edison's first work on, 24
Photographs, transatlantic, by radio, 26
Pillars of faith, 63
Pithecanthropus, as Dr. McGregor conceives him, 74
Planetarium, Adler, in Chicago, 111
Plant that eats flies, 97
Pole, North, discovery of, 42, South, 42
Porcupine, picture of, 115
Post and Gatty, their flight around the world, 11
Poultry breeding, experiments in, 17
Power boats in action, 26
Power plant, Electron, Washington, 121
Propeller-car, rear view of, 14
Puccinea, injurious fungus, 37
Puffer fish, curious habits of, 97
Puyallup River, power plant on, 121
Pyramids, Egyptian, 62

Quebec Bridge, 122

Rabies, inoculating against, 88
Radio, boy lecturer on, 26; sending photographs by, 26; for bees and butterflies, 83; running trains by, 87; use of for safeguarding miners, 92; use of in the wilderness, 107; on the lightship, 126; for the befogged ship, 127; in Fire Island lightship, 127
Radio broadcasting, marvels of, 66
Radiotron family, the, 86
Radio waves, why they hug the earth, 67
Radium, why it is costly, 22; where found and manufactured, 22; its origin, 32; found in Paradox Valley, 80
Railroad, overhead, in Berlin, 49
Rain, how formed, 41
Rain-making, progress toward, 104
Ramsay, Sir William, experiments by, 80, 81
Rats, methods of fighting, 109
Rattlesnake, no match for roadrunner, 10
Redwood trees, oldest living things in the world, 76
Reptiles, the age of, 74
Resonator, Dr. Volf's invention, 27
Ring, the most important in the world, 21
Ritterrath, M. J., inventor of cold light, 20
Rivers, why they meander, 24
Roadrunner, in fight with a rattler, 10

INDEXED CONTENTS

"Rocket," Stephenson's, famous pioneer locomotive, 47
Rumford, Count, discoveries of, 25
Ruth, "Babe," hitting a "homer," 16

St. Paul's Cathedral, London, 65
St. Peter's, Rome, 65
Sanitarium, a peculiar, 12
Sault Ste. Marie, Michigan, 123
Saurian, a swan-necked, 74
Sawfish, dangerous weapon of, 95
Schiaparelli, discoverer of canals in Mars, 30
Schmidgall, C. H., inventor of a novel auger, 123
Sea, teeming life of, 55
Sea monsters, strange types of, 79
See, Prof. T. J. J., his theory of sun-spots, 51
Self-defense, for fishes and nations, 97
Sex, scientific discovery regarding, 78
Shasta daisy, produced by Burbank, 76
Shells, wearers of, 99
Ships, built of concrete, 99
Shooting round a corner, 13
Siphon, in Los Angeles aqueduct, 54
Sky, temperatures in, 107
Skyscraper, the modern, 103; examples of in New York, 118
Sky-writing, how done, 104
Sleeping sickness, the conquest of, 29
Sling, David's, operated by electricity, 106
Slipher, Dr. E. C., his photographs of Jupiter, 90
Sloth, curious habits of, 100; fossil skeletons of, 100
Smith, Dr. Theobald, discoverer of insect carriers of disease, 109
Snakes, a little girl who plays with, 114
Snow-plow, 85
Soldier's Field, Chicago, during an Army and Navy game, 17
Spectroscope, marvels of the, 20, 100
Speedboat, at Miami, 26; pneumatic, Dr. Volf's invention, 27
Sperry, Elmer E., inventor of the gyroscope, 111, 126
Sphinx, symbol of mystery, 62
Spinden, Dr. Herbert J., expert on Maya civilization, 102
Spinning wheel, invention of, 44
Spirit of St. Louis, Lindbergh's famous airplane, 22
Spraying, 85
Stainforth, Lieutenant G. H., who flew 404 miles an hour, 17
Star, measuring a, 71
Star clusters, recent discoveries regarding, 90
Star-gazers, ancient and modern, 31
Stars, a cloud of, seen through a large telescope, 30
Steamboat, first American, 98; first commercial, 99
Steam fire engine, the first, 40
Steamship, whaleback type of, 119; the latest steamless, 126
Steel for flivvers, 24
Steel mill, typical scene in, 66
Steinmetz, Dr. Charles P., 15
Stephenson, George, inventor of locomotive, 46
Stevens, inventor of screw propeller, 98
Submarine, British, as airplane carrier, 78; latest type of, 78
Sugar, as an explosive, 46
Sun, as seen during an eclipse, 31; if our earth visited the, 50; telling chemical composition of, 50
Sunlight, use of in place of coal, 110
Sun-spots, the why and wherefore of, 51
Surgery, aseptic, 69; an early experiment in, 88
Suzette, an educated chimpanzee, 94
Swallows, cliff, and their mud nests, 57
Swingle, Dr. W. W., experiments with frog, 19
Swordfish, how it uses its weapon, 95

Telegraph, invention of, 120
Telephone, invention of, 24; diaphragm, marvelous work of, 25
Telescope, refracting, at Yerkes Observatory, 30; reflecting, at Mount Wilson Observatory, 70; the largest Canadian, 90; how to build your own, 91; Herschel's hand-made, 91
Television, marvels of, 86; two-way, 86

Tenaya Canyon, Yosemite National Park, 72
Tesla, Nikola, at work in his laboratory, 60
Thermostat, magic heat regulator, 61
Thrush, nest of, 57
Thyroid gland, its need of iodin, 28; the brain-maker, 91; experiments with, on rats, 91
Ticks, carriers of fever, 109
Tides, a machine that predicts, 84; cause of, 118
Time, curious facts about, 73
Time and space, the conquest of, 17
Tortoise, most familiar of large shell-bearers, 99
Totem ceremony, 9
Trachodon, a vegetarian dinosaur, 35
Tractor, driving out the horse, 84
Train, a topsy-turvy, 49
Train-stop, automatic, 10
Transit instrument, use of, 110
Traveling around the world in twenty-four hours, 110
Tree, personality of, 77
Trevithick, model of his locomotive, 46
Tsetse fly, carrier of germ of sleeping sickness, 29; a victim of, 29; typical home in region of, 29
Turbo-generator used in Los Angeles, 15
Turner, Captain Cyril, inventor of sky-writing, 104
Twins, facts about, 44
Type, setting by the line, 124
Typhoid fever, vaccinating against, 28

Unicycle, a strange invention, 86
Universe, the, appalling size of, 14; measuring the, 90
Utah, a garden valley in, 53

Vaccination, latest methods of, 89
Vaccine therapy, 28
Vacuum-cleaning for cotton fields, 18
Vacuum tube, the DeForest, 86
Vanadium steel, the discovery of, 24
Ventilation, conflicting doctrines regarding, 111
Vesuvius in action, 19
Virgo, a nebular region in, 30
Vital capacity, recent tests of, 89
Volf, Dr. Christian A., inventor of sound distributor, 27

Water, as a sounding board, 27; use of for power, 60; essential to decay, 85; magic power of, 105, 116
Waterfall, half a mile of, 31
Waterspout, caught in a, 52
Water-wheel, ancient and modern types of, 105
Watt, James, inventor of the first commercially important steam engine, 19; steamboat inventor, 98
Weaving, primitive methods of, 45; modern methods of, 45
Whale, white, racehorse of the deep, 95
Whaling boat, modern, 95; New Bedford whaling fleet, 95
Wherry, Dr. E. T., pure food expert, 100
Whitney, Eli, inventor of cotton gin, 44
Wilfrid, Brother, and his poultry experiments, 17
Windmills, new uses for, 82
Winnie Mae, the, on its world flight, 11
Wood, making paper from, 25
Woodchucks, 75
Woodpecker, storehouse of, 77
World, weighing the, 61
Wright, Sir Almroth, discoverer of vaccine therapy, 28
Wright, Wilbur and Orville, inventors of the airplane, 18

X-ray in the every-day world, 28; how it works, 28; its picture of the human stomach, 28

Yellow fever, closing in on, 42
Yellowstone Park, great falls at, 73
Yosemite Falls, half a mile of waterfall, 31
Young, Prof. Charles A., 50

THE BOOK OF MARVELS

Eight-Foot Giants

THERE are giants in these days —just as in all other days— who owe their exceptional size to the overactivity of a little gland called the pituitary body, located within the skull. This explanation of gigantism is one of the discoveries of modern times.

Totem Ceremony

TO the votary of any religion, the traditional observances of his faith are the most compelling of all activities. That fact, in itself, is perhaps the greatest of psychological marvels. Such ceremonials as that here pictured have peculiar interest for all of us, because they represent stages of development through which our own ancestors no doubt passed at no very remote period of the past.

Underwood & Underwood

EIGHT-FOOT GIANTS

THE ORDEAL BY FIRE — A TOTEM CEREMONY

Wide World Photograph

LARGEST AIRSHIP IN THE WORLD, THE UNITED STATES DIRIGIBLE *AKRON*, LEAVING ITS MOORING MAST AT AKRON, OHIO, WHERE IT WAS BUILT FOR THE GROWING ZEPPELIN FLEET OF THE AMERICAN NAVY

Photograph by Underwood and Underwood
ROADRUNNER BATTLING RATTLER

Roadrunner Battles Rattler

THE roadrunner is a rather grotesque but interesting bird of the desert, allied to the cuckoos. It has been seen by most motor tourists who cross the continent by the Arizona route, but not many persons have witnessed such a battle with a rattlesnake as is here depicted. The bird is said to be able to spring aside rapidly enough to avoid the stroke; and to strike back instantly, before the snake has time to re-coil. All reports agree that the snake is certain to be vanquished, if not killed. The bird's strong bill is aimed always at the back of the snake's head.

Earthquake Phenomena

EARTHQUAKES are due to the fracture of portions of the earth's crust, evidencing the instability of "solid" earth. According to the newer theories, the crust of the continents (called sial) is afloat in an underlying sea of so-called sima, and the continents as a whole are shifting their positions. Such movement involves strains that result in fissures and fractures, which may be far below the surface or may extend to the surface itself. The tremblings caused by such fractures are registered by the seismograph when not otherwise discernible. Larger fracturings or those near the surface result in the familiar and terrifying phenomena associated with the name "earthquake."

The vibration advances in a series of waves from one or more central points called foci—usually deep down in the earth. It may arise from the splitting of a great mass of rock by the strain just mentioned, or by volcanic action.

The disturbance sometimes consists of a single shock lasting but a moment, yet powerful enough to wreck a city; sometimes of a series continuing at intervals for days or weeks. Scientists have discovered that its destructive effects vary largely with the nature of the ground through which it passes and with the position of the place relatively to the focus.

No part of the globe is entirely free from earthquakes, but the regions that suffer most severely from such phenomena are those bordering on the largest oceans.

A Life-Saving Mechanism

THERE is a device known as an "automatic train-stop." It is an electrical device to be adjusted back of the drive wheels of the locomotive, to come in contact with a rail called a "ramp," which is adjusted parallel to one of the ordinary rails at a certain distance from the location of a block signal. The mechanism can use a portion of the operating battery of the standard automatic block signal system.

When the projecting portion of the automatic train-stop comes in contact with the ramp, it establishes an electrical circuit which momentarily opens the air valve; but if the block ahead is clear, the valve is automatically closed again almost instantly. If, however, the block is not clear, the air valve remains open and the brakes are applied, stopping the train.

Comprehensive tests of this mechanism are said to have been completely successful. One test was "to pass over a ramp at full speed and permit the train to make full stop against steam, as if the engineer were dead."

A SPIRAL NEBULA

The Mother of Worlds

THE spiral nebula has been dubbed "the mother of worlds," because of the belief held by many astronomers and cosmogonists that this common form of nebula represents a solar system more or less like ours, in process of formation. The nodules in the whirling arms are held, according to this hypothesis, to represent nuclei of condensation which, by gathering material to themselves gravitationally, will become planetary bodies. According to the meteoritic theory of Chamberlin and Moulton, the planets of our solar system, including the earth, were formed in this way. This doubtless is the favored hypothesis of world-origin among present-day geodesists and geologists.

EFFECT OF EARTHQUAKE, YOKOHAMA, JAPAN

Fashions in the Congo

FOR uncivilized and civilized people alike, fashion has the power of inexorable natural law. A fairly large proportion of the mandates of fashion are inherently absurd. The procedures called for are sometimes highly deleterious to health, and even menacing to life—for example, corseting the torso. But personal comfort and health yield always to the esthetic urge; and if the ideal of the moment is a wasp-waist or a drum-head lip, who shall have the hardihood to resist the mandate? The answer is that no one resists. The wasp-waist holds its own until the mandate of fashion changes. In the Congo, fashions do not change quite so rapidly as in Europe and America—which is fortunate for the wearers of drum-head lips.

FASHIONS OF THE CONGO

Walking Through Fire

IT is possible to treat textiles so that they are non-inflammable. Asbestos may be introduced as a component of textiles. The wearer of garments specially constructed of such materials may walk through fire, provided he does not inhale hot air and gaseous fumes. Death in ordinary fires usually results from such inhalation, rather than from direct burning. A person who is caught in a burning building and must escape through hallways filled with smoke should if possible cover his face with a wet towel, and even then, hold his breath if possible. The walking through fire that is sometimes done by Hindu fakirs appears not to have been satisfactorily explained. That it depends on trickery, violating no principle of physics, goes without saying.

Photograph by International
FIREMEN OF LOS ANGELES WEARING ASBESTOS SUITS

© Pathe News and International
THE *WINNIE MAE* ON ITS WORLD FLIGHT

Post and Gatty in the *Winnie Mae*

ALL previous records for circumnavigation of the globe by any method were broken by these fliers, whose progress day by day was followed breathlessly by all the world. They flew easterly, of course, to take advantage of prevailing winds, and part of the time they were within the Arctic Circle. Such a flight about the top of the world is obviously very different from actual circumnavigation of the globe at or near the equator—a feat that remains for the aviators of the (perhaps not distant) future. To have compassed the mid-portion of the northern hemisphere in less than nine days is a memorable accomplishment. Not many years should elapse, however, before the record is brought down to twenty-four hours or less by a westerly flight at high altitude.

THE BOOK OF MARVELS

THE SITE OF HOOVER DAM

HOOVER DAM AS PLANNED

Harnessing the Colorado

IT seems strange that when the wood has been cut from a forest region where no coal is available except as hauled from a long distance, there should still be hesitancy about setting the running water at work. And strangest of all it seems that men attempting to establish homes in an arid region where neither wood nor coal is available, should calmly look upon a mighty stream of water that could at once make deserts bloom and factory wheels hum, without seeming thought of attempting to use the liquid that could be made to perform miracles, but which, left to its own devices, merely mocks them.

Yet such is the social and economic paradox that confronts us when we consider the conditions that obtain in a great part of the immense region through which the mighty Colorado River tunnels its way. That a man who suffers the pangs of thirst should decline to dip up water from a river flowing at his feet seems incredible.

But such a comparison is hardly just. To secure the potential benefits of the Colorado is not a mere matter of assuming a receptive attitude; it implies, on the contrary, stripping the communal loins for a colossal labor. The famed canyons seem to beckon the dam-maker; but they invite to an engineering task of stupendous difficulties. Moreover, there are political complications, for the interests of no fewer than seven States are involved, and the needs of different regions are not always the same.

A UNIQUE SANITARIUM

A Peculiar Sanitarium

THIS unique building is for the treatment of patients by supplying oxygen at higher pressure than the normal. The sphere is 64 feet in diameter, and has five floors. It is located in Cleveland.

Drowning a Fish

"DROWN a fish!" you exclaim. "How can anyone drown a fish?"

The answer is that you can drown a fish very easily indeed— if you can lay hands on the fish. You have only to lift it out of the water.

With its head in the air it will drown as certainly as you would drown with your head under water.

You knew that the fish would die under these circumstances, of course; but perhaps you had not thought of this as death by drowning. Yet such essentially it is.

The Popularity of Gliding

THERE is no really radical distinction in principle between flying and gliding. Nor for that matter is there any radical difference in principle between flying an airplane and flying a kite.

In each case, buoyancy is attained, at the expense of gravity, by moving a plane surface over a sufficient layer of air or by moving the air under the plane surface.

So far as the principle is concerned, it does not matter at all whether the shift is made by the plane or by the air; it is only requisite that the plane shall have the support of more air in a very brief time than the quantity directly below it at any given moment.

Otherwise, in the nature of the case, no heavier-than-air apparatus could remain aloft, except for a brief period when an uprising gust of air lifted it.

Such a gust in effect compresses the air and gives it added power.

And even winds that move horizontally serve the same purpose if the plane is tipped more or less, as a kite is always, and as the wing of an airplane may be on occasion.

Indeed, an absolutely horizontal plane and a wind blowing exactly parallel to the earth's surface would represent conditions never met in practise except for a brief interval.

Of course the motor-driven airplane develops the equivalent of a wind, and the powerful modern plane may seem to disregard the actual wind.

But such disregard is only seeming.

If the plane flies in the teeth of a forty-mile gale its progress will be retarded by just so much.

Instead of accomplishing one hundred miles, for example, in the hour it will effectively cover only sixty miles.

If, however, the pilot wishes merely to remain aloft, he may throttle his engine and his machine becomes for the time being a glider.

KLEMPERER MAKING HIS RECORD FLIGHT

BEST GLIDER OF THEM ALL, THE CONDOR

Shooting Round a Corner

INVENTORS insist on reminding us of war by producing new devices designed for the killing of men. Scientific interest, nevertheless, attaches to the recent announcement of a gun that is alleged to be able to "shoot round a corner."

I speak only from hearsay, for I have not seen the instrument in question; but an account of it has been offered that makes the feat seem almost as simple as that old trick, ascribed to Columbus, of making the egg stand on end.

For what is said to happen is merely the bursting at a certain point in the air of a large projectile which releases smaller ones that scatter laterally, and subsequently explode.

In that sense, any explosive missile will send its fragments (which in case of shrapnel may be bullet-like) "round the corner."

A FARMAN GLIDER GETTING INTO THE AIR

VIEW OF THE PROPELLER CAR

Air-Propelled Locomotive

THE propeller that grips the air and pulls this locomotive is precisely like that of an airplane. It would seem incredible that narrow propeller blades could grip the air hard enough to pull a train of cars, were it not that everyone has now become familiar with the flight of airplanes. A mechanism that can lift tons of metal into the air (even with the aid of the air itself rushing against the wings of the craft) can be expected to pull a wheeled vehicle the weight of which is supported on rails. In reality, such a craft, as here illustrated, outspeeds a steam locomotive.

The Diver's Dreaded Foe

THE octopus is a member of the vast group of Cephalopods—a branch of Mollusks so named because their legs are attached to their heads. There are great numbers of fossil forms, and the modern octopus closely resembles some of these. The large species, such as the one here shown, are far more dreaded by divers than any other denizen of the ocean depths. The diver here seen struggling with one of these "devil fishes" cut his way to freedom, and was drawn up with masses of tentacles still clinging about him. Such experiences are fortunately rare.

THE DIVER'S DREADED FOE

A Really Big Universe

THIS is really a big universe if the observations of a certain star cluster, or nebula, by the Harvard astronomers are to be relied upon.

Measured right across, from side to side, so far as the telescope has yet revealed its bounds, it appears to compass the truly notable size of 350,000 to 400,000 parsecs.

But what, you ask, is a parsec?

Naturally enough, for the word is not much in vogue outside astronomical circles. No person with earth-bound ideas could have any possible use for a parsec, for the name is a short-cut for "parallax second," and means the distance at which the parallax (or apparent shift of position of a star as viewed from opposite sides of the earth's orbit) is one second of arc.

Put in figures, this is something less than two million million miles; or, stated otherwise, about 206,265 times the mean distance of the earth from the sun.

Such distances, just to name them, make one a little giddy. A somewhat more familiar way of measuring the vast spaces involved is by "light years." As light travels 186,000 miles in a second, it goes distinctly far in a year—about five million million miles.

Yet it takes light four and a half years to come to us from the nearest star. And the light from the globular star cluster, the observation of which led to the new estimate of the size of the universe, requires from 50,000 to 100,000 years to reach us. The particular rays of light that have just been glimpsed left their source thousands of years before human history began.

We are told that the new estimates make the size of our universe about two quintillions of miles—with a leeway of error of perhaps 300 quadrillions of miles.

Boiling a Kettle on Ice

THIS seeming miracle is readily understood when it is explained that the kettle contains liquid air instead of water. Air becomes liquid only when its temperature is greatly reduced. By comparison, frozen water (ordinary ice) is a warm substance. "Heat" is a term we apply to molecular activity. The molecular movements suffice to push neighboring molecules, and thus give to them motion which we term "temperature." When the temperature of a substance rises to a certain level (under uniform conditions of pressure) the substance changes from solid to liquid; or from liquid to gas. The heat transmitted through the

Photograph by Underwood and Underwood
BOILING A KETTLE ON ICE

bottom of the kettle from the ice suffices to raise the temperature of the liquid air to the volatilizing point. So the kettle "boils," though it remains intensely cold.

Outworking Five Million Men

WHEN Michael Faraday, greatest of experimental physicists, put a little electrified disk of metal between the poles of a magnet and saw it rotate, he undoubtedly realized that he had witnessed a very remarkable manifestation of the transformation of energy.

The toy itself was perhaps two or three inches in diameter, and weighed a few ounces.

The newest machine that applies the principle is 35 feet in diameter and weighs 700 tons. It is designed to transform into electricity an amount of energy equivalent to the work of 87,000 horses—generating a current that could feed 2,600,000 ordinary electric lights.

Dr. Charles P. Steinmetz made a statement which enables the layman to gain an inkling of the power of this colossal machine.

"One kilowatt equals 1.34 horsepower, so 60,000 kilowatts represent about 80,000 horsepower. Each horsepower is equal to the muscle work of 22½ men, so 80,000 horsepower would be equal to 1,800,000 men.

A GREAT GENERATOR AT NIAGARA FALLS

"But a man cannot work 24 hours a day, while the turbine can and does work 24 hours a day. Therefore the big Chicago dynamo will do the work of three times 1,800,000 men, or furnish as much energy as 5,400,000 men working in three 8-hour shifts."

The Most Mysterious Thing In the World

GRAVITATION is the force that operates universally between all masses of matter, everywhere in the universe. The law of gravitation, as discovered by the immortal Newton, is that mutual attraction is directly proportional to the masses and inversely proportional to the distance between them.

What manner of thing is this "force" that acts, let us say, between the earth and the pencil in your hand, regardless of what may intervene, or between the earth and the sun across the vast abyss of empty space?

A push or a pull, where there is physical contact, we can in a measure understand. But how can a body operate on another body without some kind of contact? What, in any event, is the nature of this "force" that so persistently tugs at the pencil, and which we cannot screen or shut off or in any wise modify? No one knows the answer to these questions. The fact that the "simple" phenomena of gravitation are everywhere observed and have been observed since men had eyes makes it only the more remarkable that no one has ever been able to put forward even a plausible theory as to the nature of the force involved.

TURBO-GENERATOR USED IN LOS ANGELES

THE BOOK OF MARVELS

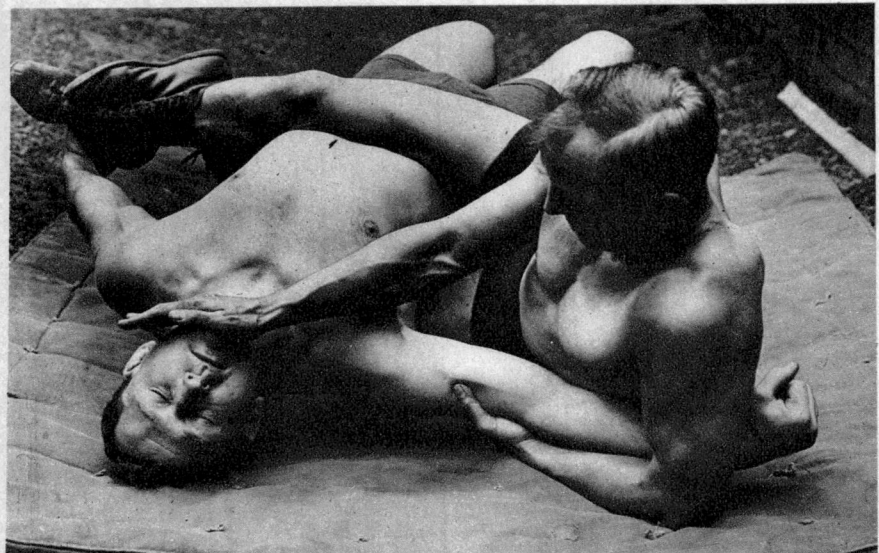

GEORGE BOTHNER, RETIRED CHAMPION WRESTLER AND HIS FAMOUS "SCISSORS-HOLD"

What Is Exercise?

VIEWING the human body with the eyes of the anatomist, we find that its chief bulk is made up of a set of bones called a skeleton, and a somewhat intricate mass of muscles, by which the skeleton is padded out to the familiar proportions of the human figure. But this padding is done in a peculiar and interesting way. If we were to dissect out any individual muscle of the several hundred, we should find that its two ends are attached to different bones, with a flexible joint between. Under no circumstances are both ends of the muscle attached to the same bone.

And then we learn that the one thing that a muscle can do is to contract, making itself shorter. As it does so the two bones to which it is attached must be fixed at the joint, so that they move with relation to each other. That the muscle swells up as it shortens (you may feel your biceps to illustrate the point) is merely incidental.

The muscles that thus move the bones about and so determine all our actions will not contract except as a nervous impulse from the brain directs them to do so. If a small area of the brain's surface is injured the muscles are paralyzed. Exercising the muscles is therefore a mental function as well as a physical function. That is a very important point to remember. You cannot exercise your body without in a sense also exercising your mind.

And so we might answer the question with which we started by saying: Exercise is that kind of MENTAL action through which certain sets of our voluntary muscles are made to contract. That is a more useful definition than one which regards only the muscles themselves.

For all-round development, the best of exercises is wrestling. The picture shows George Bothner, the most skilful modern exponent of the art of wrestling, in action. For many years, Bothner, though a lightweight, met all comers, regardless of size. His legs, with the deadly "scissors-hold," took the measure of many a giant twice Bothner's weight.

Hitting the Ball

IT is astonishing, when you stop to think of it, how large a proportion of all games that have attained great popularity consist essentially of hitting a ball.

There are only two ways of hitting any ball. You can hit it in direct line of its center or you can hit it more or less to one side of the center. The direct blow will tend to send the ball forward in the line of impact without spinning; the tangential blow will start the ball in the same line, but will impart a spin that tends to modify the line of flight and otherwise to change the results.

Older readers will recall the time when there was ardent controversy as to whether a whirling ball actually "curves" in the air; it being contended by doubters that the seeming curve of a pitched ball is an optical illusion. But no one nowadays — certainly no baseball "fan"— doubts that the ball does curve in the air. And everyone knows that the reason it curves is because it is whirling, thereby increasing the air friction on one side. When the bat hits the ball the original spin may be increased, diminished, or practically annulled, according to the point of impact; and the two factors jointly determine whether the result will be a grounder, a foul, a high fly or a straight drive.

BALD EAGLE PURSUING FISH HAWK TO SECURE THE FISH

BABE RUTH BATTING A "HOMER"

But in baseball the great art lies rather with the pitcher than with the batsman. The art of the latter is largely expressed in the design to hit the ball squarely at the center of gravity of the bat. Watch "Babe" Ruth and you see how it is done.

Conquering Time and Space

ON Sept. 13, 1931, Flight Lieutenant G. H. Stainforth of England flew his seaplane at 404 miles an hour. He probably went through the air at a higher rate of speed than was ever attained by any living thing on the earth before.

Compare his speed with other record-breaking speed tests. A human sprinter covers 100 yards in ten seconds. In the same time, a fast thoroughbred runs 170 yards; a fast trotter covers 146 yards; a carrier pigeon flies 300 yards.

But the airplane in the same time travels 1975 yards. It goes more than six times as far as the carrier pigeon.

The swiftest bird is an indifferent flier pitted against the modern man-bird. Neither in altitude nor in distance nor in speed tests could the bird compete successfully. And what bird ever equaled the Post-Gatty circumnavigation of the globe in less than nine days? There is only one kind of flying in which the bird would win—and that is slow flying. The airplane cannot slacken its speed below a certain minimum, or it will drop to the ground. Neither can the bird, of course; but its minimum is far below that of the airplane.

But even this supremacy will not long be left the bird. Soaring tests are teaching man how to keep in the air while going slowly; and the helicopter, when perfected, will enable him to stand still in the air—as one "treads water" when swimming.

In this field, as in every other, man's ingenuity ultimately enables him to outdo the best efforts of all animate competitors.

The Popularity of Games

ANCIENT and modern men alike are lovers of sport. The most famous of Roman "bowls," the Colosseum, was crowded to capacity (about 80,000 people) to witness gladiatorial contests, just as the Soldier's Field "bowl" at Chicago is crowded to witness an Army-Navy football game.

RIM OF THE ROMAN COLOSSEUM

SOLDIER'S FIELD, CHICAGO. AN ARMY AND NAVY GAME

MOUNTAIN CLIMBERS WILL HAVE THEIR FUN

Chickens Made to Order

ANNOUNCEMENT is made of the successful culmination of a series of experiments begun many years ago by a Trappist monk, Brother Wilfrid by name, at the Canadian School of Agriculture, not far from Ste. Anne de Bellevue, in the Province of Quebec.

The task that Brother Wilfrid set himself was the creation of a purely Canadian breed of poultry, better suited for Northern conditions than any breed available. He had experience of the danger of freezing combs and wattles in severe winter weather, so he determined to reduce these ornamental appendages to a minimum. He wanted heavily feathered fowls, as a matter of course, and hens that should be good winter layers, yet not too small for meat purposes. He decided on white as the most satisfactory color.

The desired new breed was to be created by intermingling old breeds, and then, as Professor Leon J. Cole, of the University of Wisconsin, has expressed it, "mixing together the available ingredients of his new breed, and by the sieve of selection, straining out the combination desired."

Brother Wilfrid selected the Cornish breed as the starting point, because it presented several of the desired qualities, including the type of comb and wattles. To get high laying quality, he naturally turned to the White Leghorn, while the Rhode Island Red, the Wyandotte and the Plymouth Rock were utilized to help winter egg production and for various other qualities.

THE BOOK OF MARVELS

THE FIRST AIRPLANE THAT EVER FLEW

The First Airplane

THIS is the original Wright "aeroplane," the first heavier-than-air machine that ever left the ground carrying a passenger, and safely returned to it. And that epochal achievement took place no longer ago than December, 1903. The other picture shows Wilbur Wright, in an airplane of the same type, making a demonstration in France, in 1908. The airplane is among the few great inventions of unequivocally American origin, and Wilbur and Orville Wright were the unequivocal inventors.

Getting into the Air

OLDER readers may recall a once-popular facetious chronicle which related that when Darius Green made his celebrated flight from the barn window, his great difficulty was encountered not in taking off but on landing.

The modern airman is not unmindful of similar possibilities of disaster.

Landing an airplane that cannot sustain itself in the air at less than a fifty- or sixty-mile speed is always a ticklish proposition.

But by the same token it is no simple matter to get such a craft off the ground in the beginning.

So when George Barbot came to us from France, bringing the "flying flivver" with which he had won a 25,000-franc prize by gliding across the English Channel, the thing about his little airplane that excited most surprize on the part of the initiated was the ease with which it got into the air.

It required but a short run for the take-off, and report had it that the two dogs running beside the craft were actually in the lead when the 400-pound plane began to mount, indicating, it was estimated, a speed of not more than ten miles an hour. Nothing like that had been seen before.

Of course, a heavy battle plane cannot be expected to duplicate that feat.

Scout planes will doubtless be constructed more or less on the model of the Barbot flivver that can take off from the decks of airplane-carriers without special apparatus to aid them; but more formidable aircraft must be given an initial impetus by a catapult or similar device when they are to be flown from a place which, like the deck of a ship, does not give opportunity for a long initial run.

A device that accomplishes this object has been tested on the battleship *Oklahoma*.

A short revolving track sustains the airplane, and permits it to be headed into the wind.

A specially constructed derrick supplies the power that gives the effect of a catapult.

The airplane is driven forward like a projectile with such force that it acquires a speed of perhaps fifty miles an hour before it leaves the trestle work. This suffices to give it initial buoyancy, and the propeller quickly accelerates the speed adequately.

Vacuum-Cleaning for Cotton Fields

THE particularity of the boll weevil is that it attacks the flower buds and young cotton bolls, literally nipping the cotton crop in the bud. As the eggs are laid and the young grubs develop in the cotton bolls, well protected, no spraying or other method of local treatment has proved efficacious in destroying the pests. It has seemed to many observers that the task of fighting the weevil is a hopeless one, and entire regions have given up the attempt to raise cotton, simply because of the invasion of this insect.

One of the newest methods of dealing with the problem is to attack the invaders with a mechanical device that is in effect a vacuum cleaner, similar in principle to the one with which every housewife is familiar.

This suction apparatus is, of course, made on a large scale, with relatively enormous pipes and a capacious dust collector, the whole mounted on wheels, to be drawn by a pair of horses.

The suction apparatus is operated by a ten-horsepower gasoline engine, driving an exhaust fan, and as the insects pass through the fan, they are dashed against baffle plates and destroyed.

THE WRIGHT AIRPLANE IN FRANCE IN 1908

Vesuvius in Action

VESUVIUS, overlooking the Bay of Naples, is the world's most famous volcano, though by no means the largest. Everyone has heard of the destruction of Pompeii and Herculaneum by eruption of this volcano. And thousands of travelers have seen it in action in recent years. The great mushroom-like tower of smoke, glistening in the sun, is among the most impressive spectacles of all Nature. The motive power that produces volcanic phenomena is heat of the earth's interior. The belching of carbon dioxid gas by volcanoes is held to be an important element in supplying this material for plant-food; which, transformed in the laboratory of the plant-leaf, becomes food for animals and man.

VESUVIUS IN ERUPTION

Growing Smaller

THE conception of growth is so naturally associated with that of increase in size that to speak of "growing smaller" seems a patent contradiction in terms.

Yet there are conditions under which a living creature may undergo development for which "growth" seems the obvious description while actually becoming smaller.

The case of the tadpole that changes rapidly into a frog under forced thyroid feeding is an illustration in point.

In the experiments of Dr. W. W. Swingle, as reported in the *Journal of Experimental Zoology*, tadpoles that normally would have retained the fishlike form for two or even three years were made to undergo metamorphosis of the most striking character in two or three weeks of thyroid feeding.

The metamorphosis consists in the development of legs and the very great reduction in size of the entire animal, including the head and body no less than the tail.

Nor are the changes by any means confined to external parts of the body.

Internal changes are equally remarkable.

For example, the undifferentiated alimentary tract of the tadpole may change in two weeks into a tract about ten inches *shorter*, comprising the stomach and intestines of the frog.

Actual destruction of embryonic tissues has accompanied the development of adult tissues.

Microscopic observation shows that the discarded tissues are in part at least literally eaten by the white blood corpuscles called phagocytes.

The old tissues thus consumed may supply nourishment for the growth of the new tissues—which might be considered to carry cannibalism to its ultimate term.

The most amazing feature of the affair is the rapidity with which the changes may be brought about at will of the experimenter by the administration of thyroid extracts, coupled with the further fact that the familiar drug iodin may be substituted for the thyroid extract with approximately the same effect.

GIOVANNI BRANCA'S STEAM ENGINE OF 1629

GUILLAUME AMONTON'S, 1699

The thyroid gland is known to be the chief handler of iodin in the bodily mechanism, but just why iodin should have such stimulative influence over living tissues cannot as yet be explained.

In counter experiments made by Dr. Bennet M. Allen and others, the thyroid gland is removed from tadpoles, and the development of the creature is indefinitely delayed.

The organic clock is here slowed down, and the tadpole may grow to large size without manifesting any propensity to undergo the normal change into froghood.

Yet here, again, the thyroid extract may be called on to exert its magic power, and under its influence metamorphosis rapidly takes place.

Iodin also may work the miracle, as Dr. Swingle has shown, though a larger dosage is required than in hastening the development of the normal tadpole.

The Steam Engine

THERE is no greater marvel, ancient or modern, than the steam engine. Heated water changes to steam, because the molecules are made to move so violently that they thrust one another apart. Such movement constitutes "heat." When expansion has thrust the piston a certain distance, the steam is allowed to escape, and may or may not be called upon to do more work in another cylinder. In any case, it condenses presently, through cooling—which means, the reduction of motion of the molecules, so that they no longer thrust one another so violently. Here we have a splendid example of the power of infinite numbers of minute particles, working together. The first commercially important steam engine was perfected by James Watt toward the close of the eighteenth century. Two earlier efforts, not commercially successful, are here depicted.

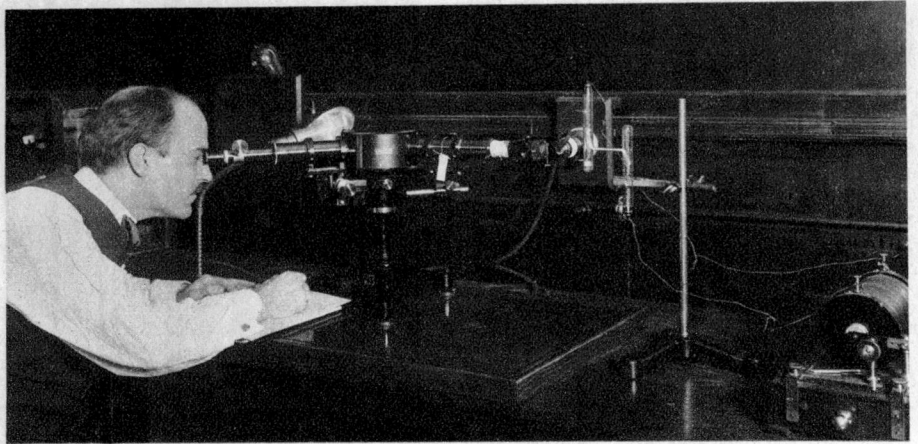

HOW THE SPECTROSCOPE IS USED

The Spectroscope

THE *Scientific American* ballot of the world's leading scientists appraised spectrum analysis among the seven wonders of the modern world. The lines of the spectrum are the earmarks of different elements. Rays of light are split by the prism of the spectroscope into the primary colors, and the tell-tale lines of any given element appear at definite points.

Clocks That Must Be Coddled

DID you ever stop to think what pains may be required to keep the clock that determines the Arlington radio signals true to the sun's course? Here it is not a case of keeping somewhere near the time for a few hours, but of keeping absolutely on the second—even the fraction of a second—day after day and week after week.

The transmitting clock (with a duplicate standing beside it, as understudy, to take on the role in case of emergency) is set to correct time at the moment of sending by slowly accelerating the pendulum with an electromagnet. This clock is connected by wires with the Naval Radio Station at Arlington, Virginia, from which the time ticks are broadcast into the ether. The ticks of the clock originate the ticking sound that you hear just before the critical hour—the thirtieth second of each minute and the final five seconds being omitted by way of emphasis, and ten seconds just before the hour, so that the final click is unmistakable.

But this transmitting clock is after all only a dummy. It would not for a single day be trusted to operate on its own responsibility. Its very location—on the ground floor of the observatory—precludes the possibility that it should keep the time with absolute accuracy; it is subjected to far too many local disturbances, such as changes of temperature and vibrational shocks.

The master clock, the really dependable timepiece, is very differently situated. It is located, in the first place, in a subterranean vault. It is mounted on a concrete base, to eliminate vibration as nearly as possible. Its pendulum is made of invar, an alloy of nickel and steel that is practically free from expansion and contraction with changing temperature. And then the entire apparatus is kept in a partial vacuum at a temperature approximately invariable, and is wound up every thirty seconds by electricity, to insure unvarying action of the springs.

Cold Light for Microscope and Movies

SOME very interesting moving pictures revealing the activities of microscopic forms of animal life have recently been exhibited. To anyone who has made micro-photographs this is puzzling. Ordinarily a long exposure is required to photograph a microscopic object, the light in the magnified field being relatively dim.

To take snapshots in sequence, which is virtually what the movie requires, would be quite impossible unless a way were found greatly to intensify the light.

And the difficulty is that when beams of light are brought to a focus, we have a concentration of heat as well, as everyone who has witnessed the operation of a burning glass knows. How to separate the heat from the light is a problem that has engaged the attention of many inventors.

It appears that a practical solution of the problem has been found by Mr. M. J. Ritterrath, of Los Angeles. He sends the focalized beam of light through a liquid filter, which shuts off the heat-bearing rays at the lower end of the spectrum.

The Blind Read by Ear

THIS machine changes printed type into articulate sounds, so that a blind person can read a book by applying it to the machine.

ASTRONOMICAL CLOCK AT U. S. NAVAL OBSERVATORY, WASHINGTON, D. C.

TWO TYPICAL SPECTRA

The Microscope

THE picture shows a compound microscope, with three "objectives," or groups of magnifying lenses, arranged to rotate into position at will of the user. The most powerful of the lenses magnify more than a thousand diameters, making minute bacteria visible, when properly stained. A much lower power makes the blood corpuscles countable. There are about five million red corpuscles in a cubic millimeter of normal human blood.

A Thousand Lamps in One

IF you examine the label on the incandescent lamp by which you are reading, you will perhaps find it labeled "25 watts." Yet the little bulb gives out a relatively brilliant light.

What, then, might we expect of a bulb of similar construction magnified a thousand times in power—a 30,000-watt lamp, in short?

Assuredly it would present a dazzling, almost a sun-like spectacle.

A THOUSAND LAMPS IN ONE

Such a lamp has been manufactured by the General Electric Company.

Perhaps the most interesting thing to note about the big lamp is the fact that the principle on which it operates is precisely that of the ordinary incandescent bulb with which everyone is familiar.

This, of course, does not mean that it is an easy task to make a 30,000-watt lamp.

There are numberless mechanical difficulties to be overcome, as is usual in building big structures; but the thing accomplished in the end is the placing of a particular part of the conducting medium of an electric circuit in a receptacle that is either a vacuum or filled with nitrogen gas, to the exclusion of oxygen.

If oxygen were present, it would rapidly unite with the substance of the filament, "burning it up"; but nitrogen holds aloof from combination and so does not produce this disastrous effect.

In nitrogen or in a vacuum, the filament glows brilliantly, as if it were on fire, but does not really burn.

The Most Important Ring in the World

HOWEVER we picture it, the Kekule, or benzene ring, is one of the most important things of which we have any knowledge, for it lies at the heart, so to speak, of every particle of protoplasm in existence. And protoplasm, as everyone knows, is the basis of every living cell in the whole range of both vegetable and animal life.

After that, it is certainly an anticlimax, but is nevertheless interesting, to note that the same ring is at the foundation of the molecules of a great variety of familiar substances, including the myriad-hued anilin dyes, such drugs as aspirin and a host of others, and such deadly "high explosives" as lyddite and the famous T N T.

In a word, Kekule's ring, named in honor of the German chemist who discovered (or if you prefer imagined) it, is the unit structure of all "organic" compounds.

COUNTING BLOOD CORPUSCLES WITH THE MICROSCOPE

THE BOOK OF MARVELS

COL. LINDBERGH'S FAMOUS AIRPLANE, THE SPIRIT OF ST. LOUIS

"WE", COL. CHARLES A. LINDBERGH

MRS. CHARLES A. LINDBERGH AND HER HUSBAND

Colonel Lindbergh's Flight

THE solo flight of Charles A. Lindbergh in the plane forever famous as *The Spirit of St. Louis*, starting from New York and landing, as scheduled, at Paris, will be known as one of the great hero-deeds of all time. It was properly applauded as an artistic no less than a heroic achievement, in that it ended exactly as planned, whereas most other successful transatlantic flights have resulted in forced landings. All the world looked on with interest when Mrs. Lindbergh, the former Miss Anne Morrow, became a pupil of her husband and presently an accredited expert. Their flight to Japan in the summer of 1931, in the new airplane with wings below the body of the machine (whereas those of *The Spirit of St. Louis* were above), was accomplished, as all the Lindbergh flights have been, according to schedule.

Why Radium Is Costly

WHEN we are told that radium is the costliest commodity in the world, we naturally ask why. And we learn that radium is costly, not primarily because it is so rare, but because so much time and skilled labor are requisite for its extraction from the crude ores in which it is originally found.

A comparatively small part of the ore dug up at the radium mines is rich enough to be worth "working." This is broken into fragments that can be packed into hundred-pound sacks, like so much coal, and shipped in carload lots to the factory where extraction is to be effected. The United States Radium Corporation has such a factory at Orange, N. J. There one finds a series of buildings with some lofts containing great vats suggestive of a brewery; other rooms with ovens and apparatus reminiscent of a smelting plant, and still others showing series of great tublike receptacles like nothing that one has seen elsewhere.

The tanks, we learn, contain the ground radium ore in a bath of sulfuric acid which will extract a considerable part of the radium in the form of a sulfate, mixed with various impurities, including barium and vanadium.

A long and tedious process ensues in which part of the radium still associated with the barium crystallizes out of the acid solution, now in the form of a chlorid; to be redissolved and recrystallized over and over, and finally transferred to yet an-

COL. AND MRS. LINDBERGH IN THE LOCKHEED-SIRIUS PLANE WHICH CARRIED THEM TO JAPAN

PITCAIRN CIERVA AUTOGIRO

other series of receptacles, this time containing hydrobromid acid, which effects the final transformation into radium bromid.

And at last in a small, sparsely furnished laboratory at the end of the buildings, after three or four months of journeying, we find what is left of thirty or forty tons of mineral in the form of a little deposit of flaky crystals in the bottom of an ordinary glass finger bowl. You could scrape the whole of it up into a tablespoon.

Verily, a mountain in labor has produced a mouse. But the mouse is worth, let us say, half a million dollars!

New Types of Airships

BROADLY speaking, only one type of airplane has until recently been in actual operation. This is the apparatus of which the Wright biplane was the type specimen, which owes its buoyancy to the principle of the flying kite, and its stability to the fact that its wings can be warped, so that they offer greater or less resistance to the air and thus serve as balancers.

But of late, very strenuous efforts have been made by inventors in all parts of the world to produce a machine to operate on a different principle. One new type is called a helicopter, because operation is dependent upon a whirling about of a helix, or perhaps two or more helices, of such size and strength as to be able to lift the apparatus directly into the air, instead of dragging it along to slide up on an inclined plane of compressed air as does the ordinary airplane.

Another new type, the autogiro, has the usual propeller and fuselage, but with the addition of airfoils that revolve horizontally above the plane, propelled merely by the wind, yet helping to support and stabilize the machine in the air. It is the invention of Juan de la Cierva, of Spain. An American-built autogiro made practically vertical landings in 1929 and attained a speed of a hundred miles an hour.

INTELLIGENCE TEST FOR IMMIGRANTS

Minds That Quit

THE much mooted army tests for intelligence were, so far as possible, selected to determine inherent capacity of mind, independent of information acquired through schooling. Yet no fewer than 15 per cent of all the men tested found an impassable barrier in the group of questions which had been found within the capacities of a normal child of eleven years; and another group of 20 per cent could not pass the twelve-year barrier.

And these, it must be understood, were not persons hitherto supposed to be defective. They were from the rank and file of the picked young men who would ordinarily be described as the flower of our American manhood. For the most part, they had doubtless been normal, average children conducting themselves in the home and in the school in a way to attract no particular attention. Their minds had simply reached a certain level and there stopped developing. Their bodies had continued to grow, and they had continued to acquire knowledge in greater or lesser degree. But their essential level of intelligence, determining effectively their status in the world throughout their lives, had been fixed or fossilized, at ten years, at eleven years, at twelve years.

Bombing the Boll Weevil

THERE are places in the South where monuments have been erected to the boll weevil—strange as that may seem. The explanation is that the weevil's threat to ruin the cotton industry led to the introduction of other agricultural industries that have proved remunerative.

But the weevil is still a deadly menace to most regions of the South, and many attempts have been made to stay its devastating march eastward and northward. One of the most successful modes of attack now is conducted from the air.

BOMBING THE BOLL WEEVIL

GRAND CANYON OF THE YELLOWSTONE FROM THE BRINK

A Meandering River

THE meandering of rivers is due in part to the varying resistance of different rocks and soils; but in part also to the tendency of all streams in the northern hemisphere to erode their right banks more than the left. This tendency is due to the same principle that causes the Gulf Stream and prevailing winds from the south to move easterly; while currents and icebergs from the north move westerly. The spin of the round earth explains all these tendencies—the fact that the circumference of the earth (or any other globe) measured parallel to the equator, increases toward the equator (see the note on icebergs). Meandering of a stream in either direction is facilitated, once the slightest departure is made from a straight course, by the physical fact that the eroding power of running water increases as the *sixth power* of the speed. That is to say, if the speed of flow is doubled, the eroding power is increased sixty four times.

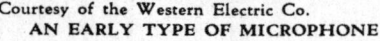
Courtesy of the Western Electric Co.
AN EARLY TYPE OF MICROPHONE

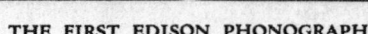
THE FIRST EDISON PHONOGRAPH

DR. GRAHAM BELL IN NEW YORK, COMMUNICATING WITH CHICAGO FOR THE FIRST TIME BY TELEPHONE

The Invention of the Telephone

GRAHAM BELL stands as the unchallenged inventor and developer of the telephone. He was born in Scotland, though his life was largely spent in America. A native-born American, Elisha Gray, filed a patent for a similar invention, his *caveat*, by an extraordinary coincidence, reaching the patent office *two hours* after that of Bell, on February 14, 1876. The telephone was named second among the marvels of the modern world in the ballot of the *Scientific American*. "Wireless telegraphy" was named first. If we reflect that radio, the culminating feature of "wireless," depends on the telephone-receiver principle for the translation of its message into sound, it would seem that the telephone should rank first. The "microphone" that transmits sounds from the broadcasting station is, as its name implies, a telephone transmitter.

The First Edison Phonograph

THIS is the first of all phonographs, this instrument being one of Mr. Edison's most spectacular inventions. What the phonograph came to be a few years later, no one needs to be told.

Steel for Flivvers

LABORATORY science makes its influence felt in the conduct of many practical modern industries. As a tangible illustration, note an incident related by Henry Ford, telling how a laboratory test enabled him to solve the problem of lightening the framework of his car without sacrifice of strength. The anecdote carries us back to the year 1905, when the early chapters of the amazing history of the Ford car were being written. At that time Mr. Ford was constructing speedsters, largely for publicity effect, and then, as always, he was eagerly studying details of construction of all rival cars.

An accident at Palm Beach during a race gave the Detroit inventor a chance to secure a little fragment (which he describes as a "valve strip stem") of a French car. He noted at once that the metal was light and strong. No one could tell what it was made of. He turned the strip over to an assistant, telling him to find out all about it. "That is the kind of material we ought to have in our cars," he declared.

Laboratory tests showed that the metal was vanadium steel—that is to say, steel in which a small percentage of the element vanadium is incorporated, as carbon is in ordinary steel. The secret thus revealed, it became necessary to send to Europe for a worker who knew how to make this kind of steel; and to induce a steel company to experiment with the high temperature requisite to successful manufacture. But the net result was that ultimately no fewer than ten different types of vanadium steel were made for use in the making of what came to be called a "flivver," and ten other types of steel —twenty types of steel in all, to meet varying needs as to strength, toughness, hardness, and so on.

Mr. Ford believes that this was the first time in the history of any large construction that the exact quality of steel to be used was determined scientifically. Theretofore, only four grades of steel at most had been used in the construction of any automobile. Thanks to laboratory tests, the varieties of steel, to meet every conceivable constructional need, are almost numberless.

How Trees Become Paper

WOOD is composed essentially of more or less spindle-shaped fibers that are in effect minute tubes composed of an organic substance called cellulose. At one stage of their development, the tubes were filled with living protoplasm; in other words, they were living cells. But in the hardened wood that makes up the bulk of the trunk of a tree, the tubes contain only granular or fibrous matter, which adds to the strength and solidarity of the wood, but serves no direct function in the life of the plant organism. The functioning tissue is merely the layer

ON THE WAY TO THE PULP MILL

GRINDERS FOR REDUCING WOOD MECHANICALLY TO PULP

Some Marvelous Bridges

MORE than a century ago an American named Benjamin Thompson, better known by his European title of Count Rumford, discovered that a given amount of mechanical energy, or work, will produce a definite amount of heat.

He proved that water could be boiled with the heat generated by boring a cannon.

James Watt taught the world how to change the energy of heat into mechanical motion with the steam engine.

Then Faraday showed how to establish practical inter-relations between electricity and mechanical movement with the aid of the magnetic field, preparing the way for that wonderful worker, the modern dynamo.

An ingenious application of the same principle enabled Alexander Graham Bell to bridge the gap between the energy of electricity in motion and the energy of sound waves, the telephone being the result.

The telephone diaphragm, which is made to oscillate by sound waves in transmitting, and which in turn generates sound waves at the receiving end by oscillating under the influence of electromagnetism, is a very sensitive apparatus, constituting a marvelous bridge between the material world (air) and the immaterial realm of the electron (electricity). Yet it has definite limits of responsiveness.

directly beneath the bark—the so-called cambium layer—and each successive layer functions thus for a single season only, a fact which accounts for the rings of annual growth visible on a cross-section of a tree-trunk.

The little dead cellulose tubules that make up the heart of the tree are what give the wood its chief value in the eyes of the papermaker. Overlapping and interlacing in the finished product, these tough fibers are chiefly what give high-grade paper a texture that resists tearing.

The process of making such paper from tree-trunks consists essentially of the isolation of the cellulose tubules from their matrix by a chemical process that renders them transparent, and then jamming them together in a thin layer with an artificial binding material (often made of ground wood pulp) to make the paper opaque.

ROLLS OF PAPER READY FOR WRAPPING

SPEEDBOATS IN ACTION AT MIAMI, FLORIDA

Power Boats in Action

GAR WOOD, speed enthusiast, in his eighth *Miss America*. Speedboat competition is so keen, and the sport has so many followers, that records are made merely to be broken. The power is so great, and the margin of safety so small, that a boat may break in two merely from hitting the wash of another boat at an unfortunate angle. This happened to the *Miss England* of Kay Don at Detroit in the international races in August, 1931.

Transatlantic Photographs by Radio

IF you were to see someone operating what appears to be an ordinary typewriter, and were to observe that the machine was producing a picture instead of a letter, you would doubtless be astonished. Astonishment would not be lessened when you were assured that the picture thus transcribed by the machine reproduces a photograph that had been taken within the half hour over in Europe. The explanation that the picture had come across the ocean in the form of a radio code would not offer much enlightenment.

Yet that phrase describes, after a fashion, the new method of sending pictures by radio that has been developed by Dr. Arthur Korn, of Berlin. The machine that interprets the code is an ordinary typewriter, merely modified so that it types dots of various sizes instead of letters. The operator who receives the code has nothing to do but strike in sequence the keys representing the groups of letters that have come by radio.

The picture thus typed out is made up of dots of different sizes, much like the ordinary half-tone printed in a newspaper or magazine. The dark portions of the picture are made up of larger dots; the light portions, of small dots; and the intermediate shades, of dots variously graded in size. The "letters" of the typewriter are dots and dashes.

It remains, however, to explain how the code of grouped letters was made at the transmitting end of the line.

The method, briefly stated, is to roll a negative of the original picture about a glass cylinder, upon which a beam of light plays intermittently as the cylinder revolves. Shadows of varying intensity are thus thrown on the surface of a cell made of the strange metal selenium, which has the curious property of transmitting electricity more readily when illuminated. A highly ingenious mechanism causes a telegraphic key actuated by the current passing through the selenium to produce the dots and dashes of the Continental Morse code in such groups as to represent a different letter for each of seventeen gradations of light, so that the letters from A to P are represented.

MISS AMERICA VIII, HEAD ON

The message sent by radio consists only of these groups of letters, and, of course, the typewriter that is to reproduce the picture is constructed with the same correspondence between letters and dots.

From the Mouths of Babes

I HAVE before me a photograph that shows a group of people of both sexes and various ages assembled in the playground of a public school, listening to a lecture. The lecturer stands beside a large blackboard on which he has made a drawing representing the antenna of a radio station. The pointer in his hand seems to indicate that he is discussing the insulation of the antenna wire. A radio receiving apparatus on a table beside the blackboard suggests that practical demonstrations are to be given in the course of the lecture.

MISS AMERICA VIII IN ACTION

THE BOOK OF MARVELS

The chief interest in the picture, however, lies not in the subject under discussion, but in the personality of the lecturer. For the individual who stands there at the blackboard holding the attention of his audience, and evidently comporting himself at once with dignity and confidence, is a slip of a schoolboy in knickerbockers; seemingly about the smallest person in the entire assembly. We are told that he is eleven years old, though he does not look it. In facial contour and expression he is a winsome child. If he were standing there reciting, "The Boy Stood on the Burning Deck," we should feel that he had been assigned a school-task rather beyond his years.

But this youngster is giving a lecture on radio!—on the technicalities and practicalities of radio, if you please. And he is fully competent to carry out the task he has assumed. Indeed, he is the official teacher of radio in the Philadelphia school that he attends.

These be strange times, my masters. From the mouths of babes, indeed, come words of wisdom.

DIVERS WORKING ON WRECK

Diving for Treasure

THE amount of sunken treasure is enormous. Every now and again a ship goes down with a cargo that includes gold bullion to the amount of millions of dollars. In ocean depths, such lost treasure is absolutely irrecoverable by any method hitherto devised. But in such shallows as the English Channel there may be possibility of salvage, though the feat is usually difficult. Diving bells were used in ancient times. In our own day, the diving suit, supplied with air-pipes, and even with telephone equipment, has been greatly improved. An ultra-modern type of suit even supplies its wearer with oxygen independently of an above-water source. But at best diving is a hazardous pursuit, with an element of awesome romance, based on the fact that the diver operates in an "unnatural" medium—an environment, however, that is often fantastically beautiful.

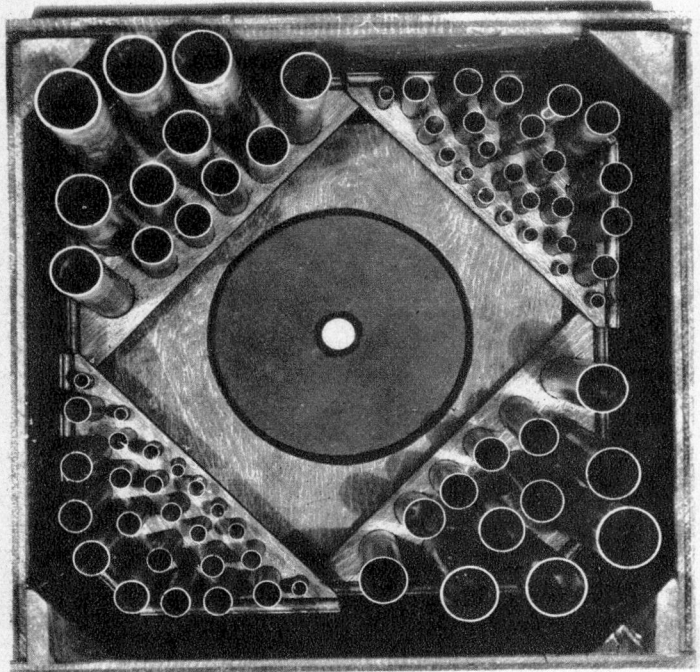

DR. VOLF'S NOVEL RESONATOR

Water as a Sounding Board

HERE is a novel resonator, or sound-distributor, designed for use in movie theaters to give improved reproduction of all sounds, vocal or instrumental. The various tubes are designed with careful regard to the scale of sound waves, following (as the inventor, Dr. Christian A. Volf, explains) the fundamental studies in acoustics of Helmholtz. This in itself is an important innovation. But the peculiar clarity and naturalness of reproduction is ascribed in large part to the use of a water surface as sounding board or reflector of the sound waves. The suggestion came from the well-known pleasing quality of singing heard across water. The application of the idea is exceedingly ingenious. The practical value of the method in bettering tonal quality in large-scale production has been successfully demonstrated in the largest of metropolitan sound-movie theaters.

DR. CHRISTIAN A. VOLF'S PNEUMATIC SPEEDBOAT

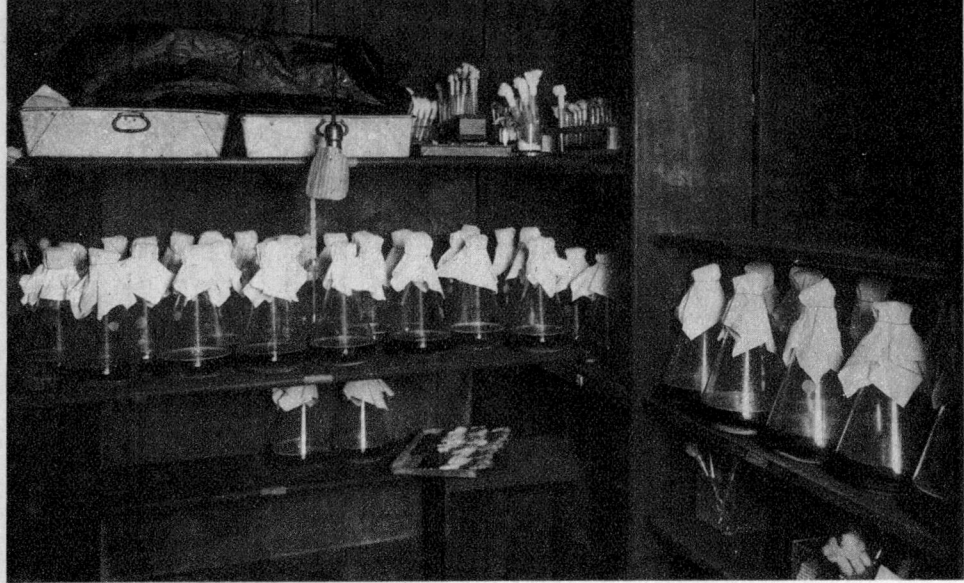
ANTI-TYPHOID VACCINE IN A CITY LABORATORY

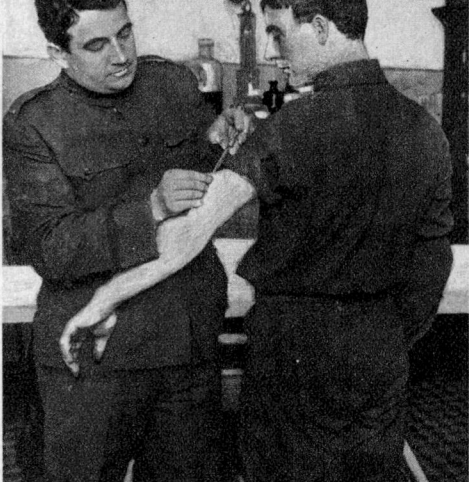
ADMINISTERING ANTI-TYPHOID VACCINE

Vaccine Therapy

AN anti-typhoid inoculation—a process that probably saved more lives in the World War than were taken by all agents of destruction combined. It may be expected that the name of Sir Almroth Wright, the originator of the method, will be remembered by posterity after such names as Foch, Von Hindenburg, Haig, Pershing, Clemenceau, and Woodrow Wilson have become meaningless or have been quite forgotten. The other photograph shows flasks of anti-typhoid vaccine in a New York laboratory.

X-Rays in the Every-Day World

WHAT is commonly called an X-ray photograph, but what the expert prefers to term a radiograph, is a shadow picture, essentially similar to a shadow cast by light shining through an object of variable translucency. Everyone nowadays is familiar with the appearance of such radiographs, revealing, for example, the roots of the teeth or the bones of the hand or foot.

Possibly you have had shoes fitted at a shop where they X-ray the foot, showing you on a fluorescent screen just how the bones are crowded out of proper alinement by too narrow a shoe-toe, and the like. And you have probably noted that metal pegs and lace-fasteners cast even deeper shadows than bones.

Or you may have had the experience of having your digestive tract X-rayed after you had drunk copiously of a milky fluid (usually a bismuth compound) which, you were told, would cast an X-ray shadow as effectively as bone itself. And from that experience you may have learned that it is not the mere hardness of any substance that makes it opaque to the rays, but its density, or, in technical phrase, its atomic weight. The soft tissues of the body are composed chiefly of hydrogen, carbon, nitrogen, and oxygen, which are elements ranging in atomic weight from 1 to 16; whereas bone has for its basis calcium, with atomic weight of about 40.

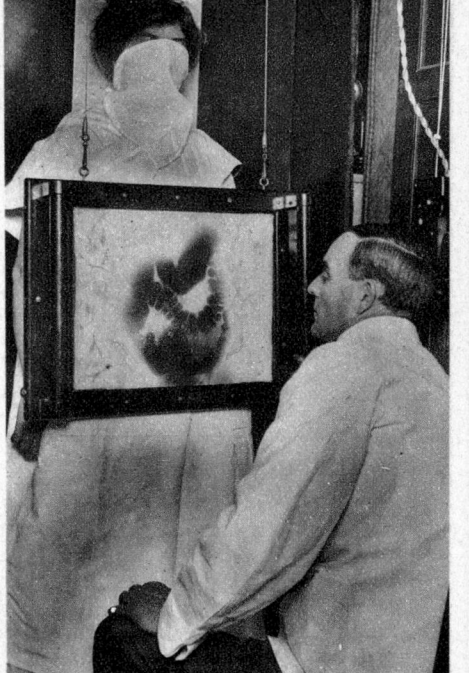
X-RAY PICTURE OF THE HUMAN STOMACH IN ACTION

That is why the X-ray so clearly reveals the shadow of the skeleton. A frame of iron casts even a darker shadow, because iron has atomic weight of almost 56; and a lead bullet, lodged in bone or elsewhere, stands out as a yet darker patch, because the atomic weight of lead is almost 207—more than five times that of calcium. It is because lead is so dense, and therefore so resistant, that screens are made of that metal to protect the X-ray operator.

Yet opacity to the X-ray is only relative. No metal, not even lead, is absolutely resistant to it. Some very short, or "hard" X-rays, notably those emanating from radium, can penetrate almost a foot of lead; and iron is so pervious that defects and impurities in plates of steel three inches in thickness may be revealed by the radiographic method, as Dr. H. H. Lester has shown at the U. S. Arsenal, at Watertown, Mass.

The steel plate or casting that poses for its X-ray picture must sit perfectly still during a thirty-minute exposure if metal of three-inch thickness is to be tested. Dr. Lester has been able to gage the exposure so closely that cavities one-fiftieth the thickness of the metal can be detected as areas of greater illumination.

Our Need of Iodin

FOR several generations the medical profession has held iodin in high regard as a medicine. In the treatment of certain chronic systemic disorders, it is almost indispensable, yet until recently no one had the slightest idea as to how or why the drug produced the observed effects. The improvement of patients to whom it was administered was often unequivocal and obvious; but in attempting to explain the action of the drug the physician had to fall back upon such meaningless terms as "blood-purifier," "alterative," and "obstruent."

In recent years, however, a clue has been gained to the manner of action of the mysterious agent, through the discovery that iodin in exceedingly small quantities is a normal constituent of the human body, and that the thyroid gland is the organ in which it is chiefly stored.

The normal functioning of the thyroid appears to be absolutely dependent upon its iodin supply, and the thyroid secretion has an important influence over every tissue and organ of the body. The medicinal administration of iodin may directly stimulate the action of the thyroid, and thereby improve the nutritional conditions of the bodily organs.

The most direct and unequivocal evidence of an iodin shortage in the body is usually to be gained from examination of the thyroid gland itself, and consideration of the symptoms known to be associated with thyroid disturbance. Most laymen are familiar with the word "goiter," implying an enlargement of the thyroid gland.

There are certain regions where goiter is peculiarly prevalent, and it was long supposed that the drinking water of such regions must contain some toxic property. Latterly, however, the opinion has gained ground that the trouble is due not to anything present in the water, but to the absence of iodin.

A VICTIM OF THE TSETSE FLY

The Conquest of Sleeping Sickness

THE report that a German physician has announced the discovery of an effective remedy for sleeping sickness must be accepted as provisional only until the results of comprehensive tests, now said to be under way in Africa, are reported. It is no new thing to have remedies reported which are expected to conquer the deadly malady, but hitherto these have not stood the test of time.

It will be recalled that the long series of experiments that led the late Dr. Ehrlich to the discovery of the famous "606" contemplated the discovery of an antidote for sleeping sickness. At one time it was believed that the arsenic preparation could be used effectively in combating the African malady; but it was found that patients to whom the remedy was administered were in danger of receiving severe injury to the eyes as an after-effect. Doubtless the experimenters with the present remedy have not forgotten that experience.

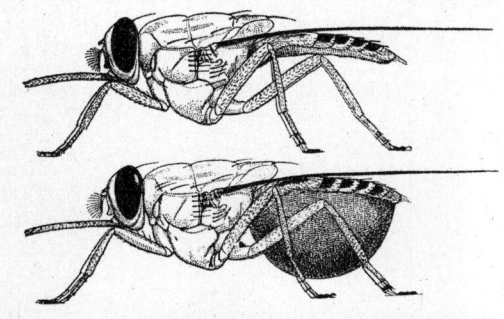

THE TSETSE FLY, CARRIER OF THE GERM OF SLEEPING SICKNESS, BEFORE AND AFTER FEEDING

The conquest of sleeping sickness would be in itself a matter of significance, but the importance of the effort extends beyond the single malady in question. The reason is that sleeping sickness belongs to a small but important group of maladies produced by so-called protozoa, or animal germs quite different from bacteria.

Bacteria, which cause the greater number of familiar contagious diseases, are classed as vegetable organisms, and it is familiarly known that the germs themselves, devitalized, may be used to make a preventive vaccine. But the protozoal germs, classed as animal organisms, have not hitherto been manipulated in the same way.

The germ of sleeping sickness, viewed under the microscope, is a relatively long, slender creature, of almost eel-like proportions. It is introduced into the body, as is well known, by the bite of a tsetse fly, which has secured the germ by sucking the blood of an infected animal. The germ is scientifically known as a trypanozome.

Developing in the human blood stream, these germs so interfere with the bodily activities as to produce the lethargy that has given the popular name "sleeping sickness" to the malady. The remedy to be desired, obviously enough, is something that will destroy the germs in the blood stream without injuring the patient. But unfortunately it has proved extremely difficult to find anything that is toxic to the trypanozome without being toxic to its unwilling human host.

A TYPICAL HOME IN THE TSETSE FLY REGION

THE BOOK OF MARVELS

REFRACTING TELESCOPE, YERKES OBSERVATORY

A Great Refracting Telescope

THE refractor at Yerkes Observatory is among the largest in the world. Refractors, using glass lenses, are not comparable in power to the great reflectors, with their mirrors, but are equally important. The refractor dates from the time of Galileo. The reflector was invented by Sir Isaac Newton.

The Inheritance of Color-Blindness

A CLASSICAL anecdote relates that John Dalton, the celebrated originator of the atomic theory in chemistry, was once astonished to discover that there existed in the eyes of most people a difference in color between the red coats of soldiers and the green grass on which they paraded. To Dalton's eyes there was no difference at all. Until then the phenomenon of color-blindness had not been recognized. The condition is even now sometimes spoken of as Daltonism, in recognition of the discoverer.

Yet color-blindness is not a rare condition. Extensive studies in Europe have shown its presence in four males, on the average, in every hundred, and in one female in two hundred. It is not uniformly distributed, however, being found to prevail in certain families.

This is another way of saying that the infirmity may be inherited. But the manner of inheritance is peculiar. A color-blind man does not have color-blind sons. Nor, usually, do his daughters suffer from the defect. But daughters, though not themselves afflicted, are said to be "carriers" of the defect, and their sons, as a rule, are color-blind. There may be two generations of such female carriers, without tangible evidence of the defect, in succession.

Our Neighbor Mars

IS the planet Mars inhabited by living beings more or less like ourselves?

Since 1877, when the sharp-eyed Italian astronomer, Schiaparelli, discovered the system of so-called "canals," this has been a moot question. No one as yet can give a definitive answer.

Unfortunately, astronomers are not agreed as to what the canal system is really like. Observers who have devoted much time to watching the planet through a telescope and making drawings of what they saw, produce pictures that do not very closely resemble the image of the planet as shown when a photographic plate is adjusted to the telescope. Most astronomers pin their faith to the photographs.

Mars With Its Supposititious Ice Cap

THE photograph presents the polar cap very distinctly. Astronomers are not fully agreed that it is an ice cap. Conceivably it might be frozen carbon dioxid. The equatorial markings are even less definitely explained.

A Nebulous Region in Virgo

THIS photograph, taken with the Barnard ten-inch refractor, shows the stars in a small space in the Constellation Virgo, the Virgin, one of the familiar constellations of the Zodiac. When we reflect that each point of light represents a gigantic sun, an awesome conception of the magnitude of the stellar universe is engendered. Only a few of these stars are visible to the naked eye. On the other hand, the great reflector at Mount Wilson would reveal thousands of stars that do not appear on this chart.

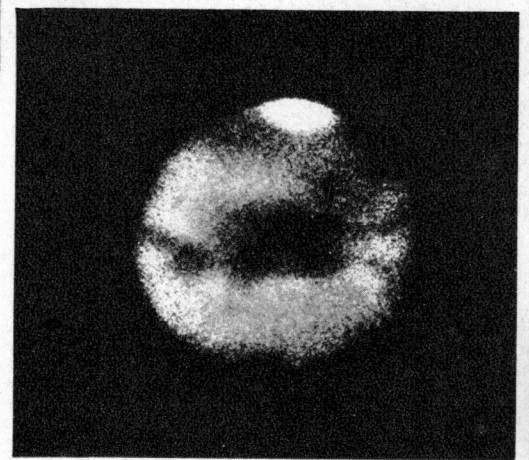

THE PLANET MARS

A CLOUD OF STARS SEEN THROUGH A LARGE TELESCOPE

THE SUN IN ECLIPSE

earth to have the same visual angle as the enormously large and distant sun. From an astronomical standpoint, it is a highly important coincidence; it determines complete eclipse of the sun now and again, and thus gives opportunity not otherwise available for the study of the phenomena of the solar atmosphere. The photograph, showing a series of consecutive exposures, reveals a vivid "corona" only when the face of the sun is completely hidden. Of course the corona is there all the time, but the negative does not show it until the brilliancy of the sun's face is shut off.

Ancient Star-Gazers

THE big modern telescopes are not much used for star-gazing or any other kind of direct observation of heavenly bodies. Some refracting telescopes, indeed, have their lenses ground in such wise as not to be suitable for use with the eye—which certainly seems paradoxical. The explanation is that no lens can be so ground as to bring all the rays of the spectrum to precisely the same focus, and that a choice must therefore be made between good focus for the relatively long light-waves, which are best for vision, and the very short ones, which best affect the photographic plate. That the latter are selected is evidence of the relative valuation of eyes and photographic plates in the estimation of the astronomer.

It might almost be said, then, that professional star-gazing is an obsolescent art. The astronomer of our day devotes his time largely to the study of negatives. His gaze is directed downward rather than toward the skies. The days of real star-gazing were the days when there were no telescopes—though of course the astronomer of necessity continued to be a direct observer until the art of photography was invented, less than a century ago. And it is marvelous, when we look back, to realize how much the early star-gazers learned about astronomy before they had magnifiers to aid the eye.

YOSEMITE FALLS—HALF A MILE OF WATERFALL

Half a Mile of Waterfall

THE Yosemite Falls, in the Yosemite Valley, are 2,600 feet high, or almost exactly half a mile—though the descent is not unbroken. The precipice over which they plunge was carved by ice and water in past ages, and the process of erosion is still in progress. Walls as nearly perpendicular as this usually tell of the action of ice in the form of glaciers. Running water works in the end no less effectively, but the walls it erodes are more sloping.

The Sun in Eclipse

EVEN to-day, an eclipse of the sun is an awesome phenomenon. In the elder day, it was an event to cast terror into every soul, coming unpredicted, and apparently presaging some dire disaster. It is a striking coincidence that the small moon should be poised just far enough from the

ANCIENT CHINESE ASTRONOMICAL INSTRUMENTS

THE BOOK OF MARVELS

NATURAL BRIDGE, CEDAR CANYON, ZION PARK

NIAGARA FALLS IN WINTER

ANOTHER VIEW OF THE FALLS

The Natural Bridge at Zion Park

NATURAL bridges are rather uncommon structures, merely because it is not very usual to find upper strata of adequate strength to support a natural arch, overlying softer strata that can be worn away by running water. Usually the arch collapses, and the bridge disappears. Here, however, is a bridge one hundred feet high, and of 115-foot span. The origin of such bridges sometimes seems puzzling, because there may be no water running under them in recent times. But they are always the product of river-erosion from the sides and below, combined with normal erosion by rain and wind. A meandering stream is the chief artificer of every natural bridge.

Niagara Falls in Winter

NO words are needed to interpret these photographs. These falls are among the most celebrated "wonders" of the modern world. They are never more awesome than in winter. The view from below the falls gives one perhaps the most convincing impression of what a glacial epoch must be like that can be conjured.

The Costliest Commodity in the World

IF someone were to show you a scant teaspoonful of white powder, looking for all the world like common salt, and to tell you that the sample is worth a hundred thousand dollars—and would find ready sale at the price—your interest would doubtless be aroused.

Your first thought would doubtless be that the exhibit does not look the part. You would probably think that your informant was joking.

The matter would be cleared up, however, when you were further informed that the harmless looking powder is not common salt but radium salt, and that there is only a handful or so of the substance in existence in the world.

And when you were informed that eighty tons of pitchblende, the original mineral in which the radium deposit was found, had been worked over with a fine-tooth comb, so to say, in order to extract the teaspoonful of radium salt that you see, you would readily comprehend the high price of the commodity. The ready market for radium is due almost exclusively to its rare medicinal value.

Tearing Down a Mountain

THE blocks of rock, still showing evidence of original stratification (in token of their sea-bed origin) are detached and crumbled by the action of sun and ice, and gravity starts them down the mountain side. The work of disintegration will continue, and the entire mountain will ultimately be transported to the ocean. This particular mountain range is in Montana, so matter from one slope of the mountain may ultimately land in the Gulf of Mexico, *via* the Missouri and Mississippi Rivers, while the detritus of the other slope is transported to the Pacific Ocean by way of the Columbia.

© 1909 by Kiser Photo Co.

TEARING DOWN A MOUNTAIN IN GLACIER PARK, MONTANA

DISASTROUS EFFECT OF DEFORESTATION

Disastrous Effect of Deforestation

THE removal of the forests from neighboring hills has permitted erosion that, in time of flood, destroyed the fertile fields of this North Carolina valley. Forests make soil. Their indiscriminate removal permits the elements to remove the soil.

The Terror of Mariners

ICEBERGS are fragments of glaciers, usually originating in Greenland, that float southward (in the northern hemisphere), and are a perennial menace to navigators. Owing to the earth's rotation, the currents that carry the icebergs, and the bergs themselves, tend to take a westerly course, rather than the straight southerly route. They melt gradually as they encounter warmer waters, but last for many months. Much the larger part of the iceberg is under water.

THE TERROR OF NORTH ATLANTIC STEAMERS

BRONTOSAURS, AS PAINTED BY CHARLES R. KNIGHT

Gigantic Dinosaurs

THE largest carnivorous beast that ever trod the earth is believed to have been one of the Dinosaurs, of the Age of Reptiles. The one called *Tyrannosaurus rex*, or king of the Dinosaurs, holds the record, so far as discovery has gone. It was more than 30 feet long and 12 feet high. The duck-billed Dinosaurs were also gigantic, but they were vegetarians. So were the Brontosaurs, which in size far surpassed even the king of the predacious Dinosaurs. The Dinosaurs thrived in the region that is now the "Great American Desert" at a time when, according to the hypothesis exposited in the present writer's recent book *The Biography of Mother Earth,* our continent was continuous territory with Asia at the west and Europe at the east, and was much nearer the equator than at present; having therefore a semi-tropical climate. As the triple continent drifted northward, progressive refrigeration made the former habitat of the saurians no longer suitable, and the Age of Reptiles (after lasting about 450,000,000 years) was superseded by the Age of Mammals, which merged, after about 300,000,000 years, into the Age of Man, the parvenu.

Eggs 300,000,000 Years Old

THE expedition of the American Museum of Natural History discovered fossil Dinosaur eggs in Mongolia. The photograph which we reproduce shows the actual discovery. The Dinosaur (giant reptile) that laid the eggs lived and died in an era which, according to the time-scale used in my recent book *The Biography of Mother Earth,* terminated about 300,000,000 years ago.

ACTUAL DISCOVERY OF THE DINOSAUR EGGS

Farming the Ocean

THE most important food plant of the oceans anywhere near the shores is a flowering plant not distantly related to the grass family, technically known as Zostera marina, and popularly called eel grass. This is the plant which accounts for most of the windrows of dead "seaweed" cast up along our Atlantic shores.

It accounts also for the great bulk of the detritus at depths up to fifteen or twenty fathoms that is the chief food supply of myriads of marine creatures. This, indeed, is declared to be the "fundamental food," playing a chief part in the nutrition of all sea creatures, at least of the northern waters. A detailed study of the subject has been made by the Danish biologist Peterson with reference to a rather shallow body of water called the Kattegat that lies between eastern Denmark and Sweden, having

HARVESTING KELP FOR ITS POTASH CONTENT

extreme length and breadth, respectively, of about 150 and 90 miles. It is estimated that the annual crop of eel grass in this area amounts to about 48 million tons, half of which is carried away by ocean currents, the remainder serving as forage for the animal life of the Kattegat.

There results the growth of five million tons weight of animals useless to man, as against one million tons weight of useful animals. One problem of the ocean-farmer is to reverse these figures.

It has been found that kelp can be gathered from beneath the water, near San Diego, California, in commercial quantities, to make a fertilizer rich in potash.

The Fly in the Amber

EVEN when extinct populations, as studied by the paleontologist, are in question, the insects still hold their own, notwithstanding the fact that they have no bony skeleton to enhance their prospect of physical immortality. From a single geological era, the Tertiary, about seven thousand species have been described, so Professor Charles T. Brues, of Harvard, assures us, with many more in collections awaiting study. And as to individual fossils, a single collection, that of the Zoological Museum of the University of Königsberg, contained more than 100,000 specimens—all beautifully and effectively preserved these odd millions of years in Baltic amber.

After reading that, and having further assurance that there are many similar, though smaller, collections in other places, one no longer wonders how the phrase about the fly in the amber became a proverb. Amber appears to have been designed especially as a tomb for insects.

DUCK-BILLED TRACHODON — A VEGETARIAN DINOSAUR

A CARNIVOROUS ALLANOSAUR OF LONG AGO

THE BOOK OF MARVELS

THE ORIGINAL SEEDLESS ORANGE TREE IN CALIFORNIA

MR. BURBANK'S "PHENOMENAL BERRY"

TENT CATERPILLAR

Plant Experimenters Rival the Bee

THE original "Loganberry," a relatively gigantic berry, was the product of a chance cross-fertilization made by an insect. The "Phenomenal" berry here shown is a cross between a raspberry and a blackberry, made by Luther Burbank. The fruit greatly exceeds either parent in size and lusciousness.

What the Tent-Dwellers Teach

MAKING a trip to my Connecticut farm about the middle of May, I was distressed to find that scores of small silk tents had been erected during my absence, and that the tent-builders themselves were making free of my property without the slightest regard for what might be the wishes or prejudices of the owner.

The tents themselves were very beautiful structures, built by caterpillars.

Time was when such an invasion of caterpillars would have been promptly checked by the activities of two species of native birds that have a penchant for food of that particular quality. If these birds were now with us they would be seen perched beside the silken tents regaling themselves on caterpillars by the score.

The Conquest of Nature

IT is recorded that there are about 175,000 acres in California devoted to orange growing. In a normal year, not far from 50,000 carloads of oranges are shipped to the Eastern markets. Such a record would suggest that California must be the natural habitat of the orange.

But of course everyone knows that, in reality, the orange was not native to California. Left to itself, the fruit can thrive only in a tropical or subtropical climate. In California it requires careful cultivation. We are told, for example, that systematic pruning is necessary throughout the life of a tree. And to obviate danger from frost, it is necessary to install smudge pots in the orchard, which put a blanket of smoke about the trees in cold weather and thus give them protection.

The navel orange, which is the most popular variety, is an altogether abnormal product, in that it has no seed. The original tree that bore this kind of fruit was a sport or freak that appeared in Brazil. As the fruit has no seeds, it, of course, could be propagated only by budding or grafting. An offshoot developed in this way was brought to the United States in 1870, and all of the navel oranges are descendants of this tree, grafted on roots necessarily grown from seeds of oranges of other types.

Plants That Conserve Water

CACTUS plants notoriously grow in deserts. But they are just as dependent on water as other plants. The difference is merely that they have learned to conserve the limited quantity of water that they find available. To do this, they abandon ordinary leaves, and have the all-essential chlorophyl distributed at the surface of trunk and branches. The aggregate surface is exceedingly small, as contrasted with the leaf-surface of an ordinary plant of corresponding bulk; and the opportunity for loss of water by evaporation is minimized. Giant cactuses are veritable reservoirs of water, and are sometimes tapped by thirsty plainsmen, who make an incision about the top of a round-headed cactus, and scoop out part of the pulp.

Coolidge Dam, near Globe, Arizona

THE Dam, which was built in 1928, has a storage capacity of 1,200,000 acre feet, and the view shows the head of water maintained by domes. The waters are used for irrigating the Florence-Casa Grande Valley as well as for generating power.

Our Enemy Puccinea

THERE is a group of very destructive plant organisms of the fungus type, which at various stages of their parasitic career utilize different types of plants as their hosts. The fungi in question bear the technical name Puccinea. The botanist sometimes relaxes sufficiently to speak of them as cup fungi; and insofar as they are known to the layman they are usually called "rusts," and are scarcely recognized as living organisms, but only as manifestations of diseased conditions of the leaves or stems of the plants on which they grow.

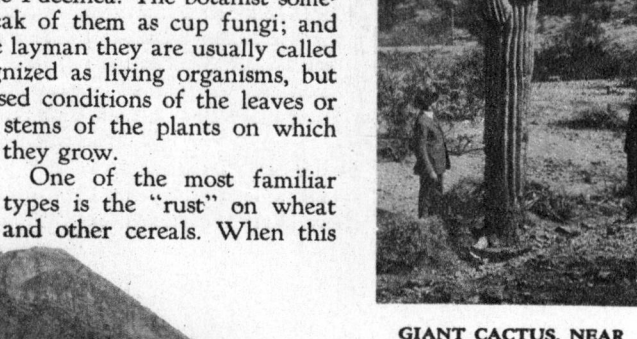

One of the most familiar types is the "rust" on wheat and other cereals. When this invades the wheat field it mars the stalk of the grain and greatly reduces the crop. But the tiny plant cannot spend its entire life on the wheat stalk. It must pass through a stage when it lives on the leaf of the barberry, where it develops minute cup-like formations, filled with spores. That is why destruction of the barberry hedges may rid a region of the wheat rust, and thereby add to the acreage of grain and tend to reduce the price of flour.

A closely allied form of fungus blights the white pines of New England after having chosen for its nursery the leaves of currant and gooseberry bushes. It was recently reported that groups of college students had been sent out to spend their vacation in destroying currant and gooseberry bushes in the hope of thus saving the valuable pines in the neighboring forest.

VARIOUS SPECIES OF CACTUS, BURBANK EXPERIMENTAL GARDENS, SANTA ROSA, CALIFORNIA

GIANT CACTUS, NEAR PHOENIX, ARIZONA

THE COOLIDGE IRRIGATION AND POWER DAM

Photograph, Keystone
BLIMPS OVER MANHATTAN

AN EARLY FLYING BOAT

THE DORNIER DO-X, THE LARGEST SEAPLANE

New York's First Blimp

THE small army "Zeppelin" or dirigible balloon is a very manageable craft, in ordinary weather. Blimps are too common to-day to attract attention. But the first dirigible that ever flew over Manhattan, only twenty-odd years ago, is remembered by thousands of observers—few of whom dreamed that the airship would ever attain the position it now holds.

Flying Boats

ONE of the earliest of flying boats is here contrasted with the newest, the monster DO-X, which flew from Europe to America in the summer of 1931. The DO-X should be regarded as a peace envoy; for it is not very difficult to realize that a flying ship that can carry a hundred passengers could, if occasion called for it, substitute explosives or lethal gases of corresponding weight. We are told that one ton of the liquid called "diphenylchlorasine" could be sprayed over an area three and a half miles long by one hundred feet wide, and would leave nothing alive in the area. A small fleet of planes like the DO-X could account for the entire population (to the last rat and cockroach) of a city like Paris or London or New York. Such a demonstration, made in the next great war, will be a salient argument for world-peace.

A New Era in Ballooning

A SCIENTIFIC discovery that augurs a new era in ballooning was made toward the close of the war. It consisted in the discovery that certain natural gases in this country contain a considerable proportion of the non-inflammable gas helium, which can be isolated at a cost within reason, so that sufficient supplies of it may be obtained to fill large balloons.

Helium, the "sun-element," is so named because it was discovered in the sun, with the spectroscope. The discovery was made by Sir Norman Lockyer. A good many years later helium was found in small quantities in the earth's atmosphere by Sir William Ramsay. But the total quantity of it isolated until very recently was only a few cubic feet, and the expense of producing it was prohibitive.

The fact that certain gas wells in this country contain helium in relatively large quantity gives our military authorities an advantage of tremendous significance. It can scarcely be doubted that the helium balloon will play a determining part in military affairs of the future.

The thing to be desired, of course, is that the existence of a fleet of helium-inflated airplane carriers with an indefinite radius of operation may be instrumental in preserving peace. But should war unhappily be declared, the same agencies may exert a preponderant influence in bringing hostilities to a quick termination.

The Dirigible Balloon

THE dirigible balloon, like the airplane, is a development of our own century; though tentatives were made as early as 1872, notably by Dupuy de Lome, in France, using manpower to operate the propeller. A spectacular demonstration was made at Paris by Santos Dumont in October, 1901—who won a prize by circling the Eiffel Tower from a neighboring park, and returning within a half hour. He was thirty seconds within the time limit, and won the hundred thousand francs. Ten years later, tourists could make the trip up the Rhine in large dirigibles, properly termed Zeppelins, as they were the outgrowth of the inventing genius and perseverance of Count von Zeppelin, the German whose first partial success was attained in July, 1901, and whose later efforts were world-famous. Long voyages of the Zeppelins are a commonplace, and the round-the-world tour of the *Graf Zeppelin* in 1929 must have made every thoughtful person reflect that the great dirigible has come to be an engine of potential destruction beyond the dreams of its inventor—who could hardly have forecast the discovery of non-inflammable gas (helium), and the development of easily-prepared lethal gases capable of wiping out the entire populations of cities.

THE *GRAF ZEPPELIN*

THE *GRAF ZEPPELIN* AT HOME

Gripping the Air

IF you swing your arms about your head, however vigorously, you note that the atmosphere seems to offer practically no resistance. It is "thin as air," and you get no grip on it.

PROPELLER BLADES

Suppose, now, that while making this test you are standing in front of an overgrown, clumsy automobile that has hitched to the front of it a largish double-bladed canoe paddle, pivoted at the center. You ask what the paddle is there for, and you are told that it is called a propeller, because when it is whirled about, somewhat as you whirled your arms, only faster, it will grip the air so hard that it will lift the big vehicle to which it is fastened—a vehicle obviously weighing several tons and carrying half a dozen passengers—right off the ground and carry it up into the sky, where it will fly like a bird.

That a whirling blade can grip thin air hard enough to pull tons of metal into the sky, even with the aid of kite-like wings, is a marvel of marvels, at which the thoughtful observer never ceases to wonder.

Frankly, the thing is incredible. Personally, I never see an airplane without finding myself precisely in the position of the traditional countryman viewing his first giraffe. "There ain't no such animal as an airplane," I say; and when the weird craft soars into the air, even though I may be aboard it, I am in no wise convinced that less than a miracle is happening. That a little whirling boat paddle should grip thin air hard enough to lift tons of weight into the sky is a phenomenon that common experience forbids one to accept as merely "natural."

CLIFF DWELLERS OF MANHATTAN

The Electric Light

THE Edison incandescent bulb needs neither description nor picture; but these photographs are thought-provocative, suggesting the changes in salient aspects of modern life to which the electric light has contributed. The electric light is perhaps not quite so essential for skyscraper life as the telephone, but it is highly important.

The Mysterious Dynamo

EXPERT electricians and practical mechanicians know how the dynamo works and can formulate certain principles of action to which it conforms. But no one knows why it works as it does, or why it works at all. Few imaginable things could be more mysterious than magnetism, which comes from nowhere and goes nowhere, yet is ever present, and which joins hands with that other mysterious agency, electricity, in the most curious of all coalitions, to accomplish miracles of work.

Long ago a wise man divined that the earth is a gigantic magnet; and more recently another wise man declared that the electron, the "unit particle" of electricity, is also a magnet. Perhaps all rotating bodies are magnets. Anyway, certain metallic bodies, actuated by electricity, are magnets, and they exert a reciprocal action on other electrified bodies. Adjust one of the bodies around the other, and make one of them stationary and the other movable, and the electric current hurtling through them is translated into rotary motion of the movable body. Connect this body to the shaft between a pair of wheels and we have the essentials of a trolley car.

But no one knows why. We only know that it is so. The explanation remains to seek. It is a mystery story that ends in mystery, like Frank R. Stockton's famous "The Lady or the Tiger!" Nevertheless, we all ride on trolley cars without feeling that we are doing anything wonderful, and the only time there is any news interest in dynamos is when a particularly big new one is constructed.

The First Steam Fire Engine

IF one were not cognizant of the spirit of conservatism that dominates human activities, one might be surprized to learn that the first steam fire engine dates from 1830. The appearance of the essential part of the device suggests that the inventors harked back to the steam engine of Hero of Alexandria for their model. Not so bad an idea at that, for the steam-kettle of Hero was reputed to do rather remarkable things — like opening and closing doors in the temples, and otherwise aiding the priests to perform their necromancies.

After Greek civilization waned, many centuries elapsed before anyone duplicated Hero's feat, and no advance beyond it was made until the eighteenth century—the time of Newcomen and Watt.

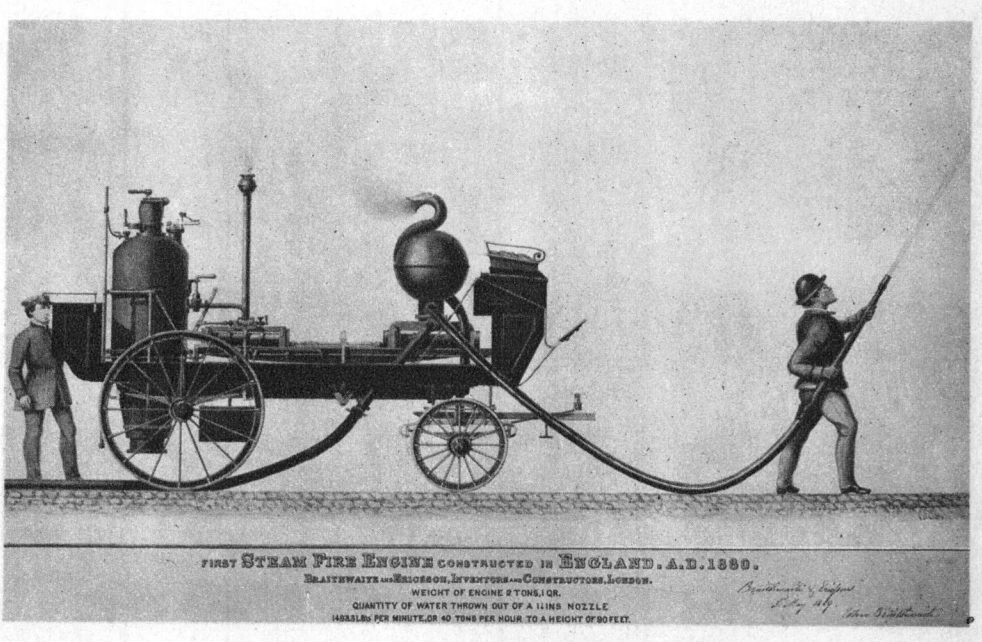

TOWER OF THE METROPOLITAN LIFE INSURANCE BUILDING, NEW YORK

ENGLISH STEAM FIRE ENGINE OF 1830

Clouds and Rain

FAMILIAR as they are, clouds are to most of us more or less mysterious. Yet the underlying principles of their formation are simple. Air at any given temperature will hold a definite amount of water vapor. Lower the temperature, and the vapor condenses as water. Such condensation is greatly facilitated by the presence of nuclei or specks of matter. Such exceedingly minute particles are always present in the air. They break up the rays of light, and cause the sky to appear blue overhead, and sometimes orange or crimson toward the horizon — the latter effects being accentuated by the presence of water vapor at the point of condensation. When condensed droplets become large enough to respond to the pull of gravity actively, they fall as rain, or as hail or snow, according to the temperature of the lower atmosphere. Clouds, then, are merely aggregations of partly condensed water vapor. And this vapor comes originally from evaporation of water from the surface of the earth — not merely from the ocean, but from all moist surfaces. Even ice evaporates, to form water vapor. Since water consists of two parts hydrogen to one of oxygen (hydrogen being the lightest of all elements), its vapor, while truly gaseous, is lighter than the earth's lower atmosphere, and so rises into "cloudland." The Dolomite mountains in the picture owe their form chiefly to erosion by water that has fallen from clouds in past ages — and the work of rock-sculpturing is still going on, as fast as ever.

CLOUDS OVER THE DOLOMITES

Courtesy of the General Electric Co.
WATER-DRIVEN DYNAMOS AT SPOKANE, WASHINGTON

THE FATHER OF DYNAMOS

The Evolution of the Dynamo

WHEATSTONE'S original dynamo, a laboratory toy worked by hand; and the dynamos in the Power House at Spokane, Washington, operated by water power. Only about half a century between them— but what a contrast!

Ingenuity Versus Muscle

EVERYONE knows the story of Archimedes, who asked only to be given a fulcrum on which to rest his lever that he might move the world.

It is one of those anecdotes that are assured perpetuity because they express in graphic manner truths that are fundamental.

It is literally true that a human being could move the world from its orbit if he could be given a strong enough lever and a place on which to rest it.

Always remembering that nothing is said about the distance to which the old globe is to be moved.

It is inherent in the principle that the distance to which an object can be moved with a lever is inversely proportionate to the increase of power.

If the long arm of the lever is ten times as long as the short arm, your strength will be enhanced ten-fold, but for every foot that your hand moves, the object you are lifting will rise only one-tenth of a foot.

All this is to the last degree elementary, yet the restating of the simple principles of mechanics never seems superfluous, so few people seem to bear them in mind after their school days.

The person who fully grasps the import of a comparatively few of these fundamental principles, is, however, in position to exercise inventive ingenuity, if he has it, with prospect of developing something new and useful.

A case in point, which prompts these comments, is furnished by the report of a new device for the prosaic but extremely useful purpose of pulling up the stumps of trees.

The new method is claimed to be highly efficacious. Yet it involves no principle newer than the use of the old, familiar lever.

ADMIRAL PEARY, DISCOVERER OF THE NORTH POLE. (1909)

Admiral Peary's Conquest of the Arctic

ADMIRAL PEARY, accompanied by Mathew H. Henson and four Eskimos, was the first explorer to reach the North Pole, April 7, 1909. Photographs of Arctic regions give one at least a faint inkling of the difficulties encountered. The region of the Pole is a sea covered with floating ice.

Closing In on Yellow Fever

AN official report on the activities of the Rockefeller Foundation tells of the progress of the ambitious project of its International Health Board, to drive yellow fever from the world. Nothing quite like this campaign was ever attempted before.

The case of the yellow fever germ is exceptional in that it depends exclusively on a particular insect to transport it to the blood stream of the human being who is its unwilling host.

This insect is a mosquito of the genus Stegomyia, and the female alone is the culprit. Proof of this fact was given in a series of notable experiments made by American Army medical officers, in Cuba, in 1900. It became clear that, if this mosquito could be deprived of a place to lay her eggs, in any given region, the yellow fever germ must fare badly. And it was proved by General William C. Gorgas, first in Cuba and then in the Panama Canal Zone, that by draining swamps and putting kerosene on the water of other breeding places, with the additional precaution of screening windows against the mosquito, yellow fever could be controlled to the point of practical local eradication.

General Gorgas believed that similar methods might be used successfully at other centers of infection. His report on the conditions in South America led to a decision on the part of the Rockefeller Board to attempt to eradicate the malady altogether. Steadily, and as it seems surely, the workers are closing in on the pestiferous Stegomyia, and now only a few relatively small infection areas remain on the Western Hemisphere.

ROALD AMUNDSEN, DISCOVERER OF THE SOUTH POLE. (1911)

Amundsen Conquers the Antarctic

THE South Pole was first reached by Captain Roald Amundsen, of Norway, accompanied by four of his countrymen, December 16, 1911. He found the polar region a high plateau, ten thousand feet above sea level. Mountains with peaks fifteen thousand feet high guard the pole. The heroic but ill-fated Scott reached the pole, only to learn that Amundsen had preceded him. Admiral Byrd flew over the South Pole from "Little America," as he had previously flown over the North Pole. He and Amundsen alone have been at both top and bottom of the world.

The North Polar Flight of Admiral Byrd

THE feat of flying to the North Pole and returning to a land base without accident was an accomplishment not soon to be forgotten. It was a performance calling for courage of the highest order, considering what must almost inevitably have been the consequence of a misbehaving motor—a possibility always, even if not a probability. The contrast between the air-method and the surface-journey of Peary and his companions, the only persons to reach the pole before (1909), illustrates strikingly the scientific progress of the early twentieth century.

Admiral Byrd's Ice-Breaker

THE ship that carried the Admiral Byrd expedition to the Antarctic is not in itself a marvel, though a very interesting craft. But it becomes marvelous, in view of its share in making history. Of course, the final lap of the Antarctic trip, compassing the South Pole itself, was made by airplane. But the airplane operated from the base to which the ship carried the explorers. Admiral Byrd thus flew over the South Pole, which Roald Amundsen reached by land in 1911.

Seeing the Invisible

EVERYONE knows how radio has extended our knowledge in the direction of long waves. The story of the recent extension of exploration in the other direction is not so well known, because as yet it has had no practical application. Yet this achievement is at least as wonderful as the other. It enables the physicist almost literally to see into the interior of the atom—the structure that until somewhat recently was regarded as the indivisible building stone of creation.

A new method of procedure now in effect enables the experimenter to dissect the atom, or if you prefer, to explore it, by shooting into it electrons liberated in an X-ray bulb under very high potential. A so-called crystal-grating spectrometer, invented by the German physicist, Laue, serves to interpret the record, which finds tangible presentation on the photographic film in the form of spectrum lines that shift position with each successive element.

The ether waves thus made visible, in case of the heaviest known element, uranium, are sent out at the rate of thirty billion billions per second. If we recall that a transatlantic radio station may use a generator oscillating 50,000 times per second, we gain an inkling of the range of variation of the ether waves now brought within the observation of the physicist—all but the tiniest portion of them quite beyond reach of the unaided sense organs.

ADMIRAL BYRD, WHO FLEW OVER NORTH POLE

THE TRIUMPH OF ADMIRAL BYRD

Lower Broadway When Admiral Byrd Returned

WHAT would a Roman general, triumphing after his foreign victories, have thought of a reception such as this photograph shows on the day of Admiral Byrd's triumph?

THE BYRD SHIP, *CITY OF NEW YORK*

ARKWRIGHT'S ORIGINAL DRAWING FRAME

An Early Cotton Gin

THE cotton gin of Eli Whitney ranks among the great inventions that have contributed to the advance of modern industry. With its use, a man could separate fiber from seeds of the cotton boll by the hundred weight instead of by the pound. The "gin" consists essentially of a series of circular saws set close together on an axle, playing between narrow slots in a comb-like piece of metal. The seeds are left behind, and revolving brushes deliver the cotton fiber as fleecy cotton down. It is interesting to note that the inventor, a northern lad, recently graduated (in 1789) from Yale College, had never seen a cotton boll at the time when he undertook to devise a machine for "ginning." His first effort was an unqualified success. The machine for baling cotton is mechanism of importance, but its invention did not call for genius comparable to that of the maker of the "gin."

AN EARLY COTTON GIN

About Twins

THERE is a popular superstition, seemingly widely prevalent, to the effect that twins are likely to be infertile. Albert Edward Wiggam, himself a twin, in writing about twins in the *Journal of Heredity,* tells of one woman who was led to question the validity of this belief. She had, indeed, always heard that if she married a twin she could have no children; but when she made the experiment, according to her own report, her "first baby was a set of triplets."

Mr. Wiggam presents two family charts, in both of which twins are shown to happen with disconcerting regularity—not, perhaps, in any predictable ratio, but far too often to be accounted for by mere chance. Such records leave one puzzled as to how the superstition about the infertility of twins originated. Perhaps some satirist or practical joker was at the source of it. The real wonder is, however, that the idea could gain vogue, considering that almost any community can boast of the presence of twins who have large families—or could do so in the day when large families were the fashion.

It is well known to students of heredity that twins are of two radically different types. There are twins that no more closely resemble each other than do average children of one family; and there are "identical" twins. The latter are always of the same sex, and, as the name implies, they are similar to the point of seeming identity. The resemblance extends to mental traits no less than physical.

In the view of the biologist, "identical" twins result from an accidental division of the maternal ovum at the very earliest stage of development. Each half of the bisected fleck of germ-plasm contains precisely the same potentialities of development. So in a sense there is no mystery at all about the close resemblance of such pairs of twins—except the great central mystery that enshrouds the primal fact that a speck of protoplasm can contain within its microcosm assured potentialities of future development along predetermined lines. But that is the mystery of mysteries.

Lace-Making Extraordinary

IT may not seem extraordinary to the lace-maker herself, but a commonplace task with which she has always been familiar. But to a masculine observer, at any rate, the making of lace by hand, with meaningless bobbins for guides, seems a feat bordering on the miraculous.

Machines That Spin

THE art of making thread or yarn out of plant fibers or the wool of sheep was a prehistoric invention of the first water. The spinning wheel here represented was the property of Richard Arkwright, and is now preserved in the South Kensington Museum, London. It is of a type first introduced about 1530. The thread of cotton or wool passes through an eye in the axis of the spindle and is subsequently wound on the bobbin which rotates on the same axis but at a different rate of speed. The rotation of the spindle twists and strengthens the thread, and the difference in speed of revolution between the spindle and the bobbin results in winding the thread about the bobbin. The spinning wheel is still in use in many outlying districts of Europe, as suggested by the photograph of the Belgian peasant

AN OLD-FASHIONED LACE WORKER

presented below. The even more primitive method of spinning with distaff and spindle, without the aid of a wheel—the spindle being rotated by the fingers in place of machinery—is also still extensively practised by the peasantry of various European countries. The first important advance upon the old way of spinning, and the invention that led to the revolution of the art, was due to Sir Richard Arkwright. The drawing frame here shown was made by him about 1780. It was commonly known as the "lantern" frame, owing to the fact that the sliver-can employed has an opening in the side closed by a door through which the sliver was removed, and so somewhat resembles a lantern. The process of drawing is accomplished by passing the wisp of cotton fibers through two pairs of rollers that nip it, the second pair revolving more quickly than the first. The distance between the two pairs of rollers is rather more than the length of the fibers, so that the drawing only slides the fibers upon one another without stretching or breaking.

Primitive and Advanced Methods of Weaving

ONE figure shows modern Persian weaving rugs. The other figure presents a modern weaving machine, which, without the introduction of any new principle, performs the operation of weaving with enormously increased speed, and produces a rug much more uniform in texture. The art of weaving was of prehistoric origin—and the principle involved has not changed throughout the centuries.

MODERN WEAVING
(Perforated Pattern Guides at Left Above)

Concerning Hay Fever

EVERY victim of hay fever should be informed that it is usually now possible to ascertain the precise cause and to administer preventive treatment that may give immunity wholly or in part.

This does not apply to all cases, but is worth trying in every case.

The diagnostic measure consists in vaccination with extracts of the pollens of various plants, to determine which one is the noxious agent in your particular case.

Observation has shown that there are four chief types of vegetable offenders; namely, the grasses, the rag-weeds, the chenopods, and the wormwoods.

The grasses, and notably timothy, are chiefly responsible for spring types (justifying the name "hay" fever); while the rag-weeds account for the greater part of remaining cases, particularly in the eastern part of the country.

As a rule, an individual sufferer is subject to the malign influence of a single botanical group.

The inoculation test (made with hypodermic needle or by scratching the skin and rubbing in the pollen) having shown the type of protein to which you are unduly sensitive, preventive treatment consists of repeated inoculation with extracts of the same protein, in graduated doses.

The principle is that of protective immunization against typhoid fever and other bacterial maladies; the human organism being stimulated to develop protective agents within the blood stream.

Another way of stating the case is to say that the organism becomes desensitized.

In any event, in successful cases, the individual ceases to be susceptible to the toxic influence of the pollen that hitherto has made his life more or less a burden in recurring summer seasons.

It is hardly necessary to add that both diagnostic inoculation and subsequent treatment should be undertaken only by a competent physician.

The method originated in the laboratory of Sir Almroth Wright, the celebrated developer of anti-typhoid immunization, as long ago as 1910.

THE OLD WAY OF SPINNING

PERSIANS WEAVING RUGS

Early Locomotives

THE steam-propelled vehicle of Trevithick was patented in 1802—twenty-seven years before the famous contest that was won by Stephenson's "Rocket." The second figure shows a commercial steam engine that ran on rails in England in 1825. The "Royal George No. 5" was in operation in 1827, at which time, as we elsewhere show, steam automobiles were operating commercially on English roads. Stephenson's task was not to invent, but to improve, the steam locomotive. He succeeded so well that his predecessors are all but forgotten. Fortunately some of the earlier locomotives were preserved. Those here shown, and various others, are to be seen at the South Kensington Museum, London.

Sugar and Flour as Explosives

EVERY now and then "spontaneous" explosions occur in sugar refineries, flour mills and granaries, as well as in coal mines and a few other places in which the air may become filled with certain kinds of dust. Such explosions are, as a matter of course, likely to be disastrous to property and life. They constitute a menace that is one of the recognized hazards of certain callings.

Of course, sugar and flour, under ordinary conditions, are not explosive. They are inflammable, however, and it appears that almost any substance that will burn may become explosive under certain conditions.

ORIGINAL MODEL OF TREVITHICK'S ROAD LOCOMOTIVE

STEAM LOCOMOTIVE OF 1825

One of the conditions is met if the substance is reduced to a very fine powder, so that it presents in the aggregate a very large surface to the air.

An explosion, technically interpreted, consists merely in the rapid turning into gas of a solid substance. The question of rapidity of action is all-important.

Ordinary gunpowder, if put into small piles in the open, will burn harmlessly. Dynamite, on the other hand, explodes with disruptive suddenness even if unconfined. Cordite, the high explosive so extensively used by the British, may be made to act more or less rapidly accordingly as it is fashioned into small string-like pieces or into large ropes.

Most other explosives used as propellants may be similarly modified in action according to relative fineness of grain. Thus cannon "powder" is used in nuggets, whereas rifle cartridges are loaded with granular powder.

Hand grenades and bombs have their contents graduated to meet specified requirements. Too fine a powder would disrupt them into fine splinters that might serve their nefarious purpose less efficiently than the larger fragments that would result from less rapid explosion.

But always and everywhere it is a question of exposed surface. A given quantity of nitroglycerine, as a liquid, exposes a relatively small surface to the air. Let it be absorbed by a spongy material, and it is in effect broken into myriad fragments, bathed everywhere in air. That constitutes dynamite.

A portion of flour packed into a bag or a cup is only mildly inflammable. But scatter it through the air, so that every dust-like particle is bathed in oxygen, and it may become a veritable explosive.

"ROYAL GEORGE" LOCOMOTIVE

A Strange Motorcycle

MANY strange vehicles have been devised, but seldom one more anomalous than the one-wheeled motorcycle invented by Urbano Cislaghi, an Italian policeman.

It is an apparatus that departs radically from all antecedent models—a "trick" machine, if you will, yet a vehicle that is said to be capable of carrying its inventor along the road at a thirty-mile clip.

The one wheel is only half a wheel at that, for it has neither spokes nor hub. Its rim is like a big bicycle tire about five feet in diameter. And the inner side of the rim is in effect a circular railway track, for the little wheels attached to the electric motor rest on it and run along it much as the wheels of a car run on an ordinary track—with the notable difference that in this case the track moves and the little revolving wheels stand still.

The motor part of the apparatus is much like that of any other electric motorcycle, albeit distorted in shape to fit inside the big wheel; but the chain-and-sprocket driven wheels of the machine are only a few inches in diameter.

The drive wheel revolves like the drive wheel of any other motorcycle; but inasmuch as it rests on the interior of the rim of the big wheel instead of on the ground it can do no more than push back on the rim as an ordinary wheel pushes back on the ground.

As the operator meantime is perched on his seat inside the revolving railway track, where the spokes would ordinarily be, he is naturally carried along.

Whether his odd vehicle has merits that will put it in practical competition with ordinary motorcycles remains to be seen.

Stephenson's "Rocket" and Its Rivals

THE "Rocket" won and became the most famous of locomotives. But the competitors are not forgotten. The second photo shows a close-up of the "Rocket" after it was remodeled—its cylinder adjusted in more nearly horizontal position. The "Novelty" (below) was not very appropriately named, for it is obviously modeled after the much earlier steam locomotive of Cugnot, which ran on the roads of France toward the close of the eighteenth century. To show the progress of a century note the engine of the "Broadway Limited," of 1931.

A LOCOMOTIVE OF TO-DAY
THE BROADWAY LIMITED

THE "ROCKET"

THE "NOVELTY" (1829), COMPETITOR OF THE "ROCKET"

An Aboriginal Souvenir

THE American Indian exercised many practical arts involving a high degree of craftsmanship. Witness the bow and arrow, garments of leather ornamented with porcupine quills, the moccasin, the snowshoe, and the birch-bark canoe.

A good many of the aboriginal arts were copied by the white settlers of Colonial days, but most of them were discarded as no longer useful in competition with developments of the nineteenth century. Offhand, one recalls scarcely any device except the snowshoe that has not been superseded in general usage by a superior mechanism.

Yet there are local regions where certain of the primitive arts of the Indian have not been forgotten. Hickory bows and buckskin moccasins and birch-bark canoes are not quite obsolete, and there is at least one thoroughly practical device of Indian origin for which no wholly satisfactory substitute has been found. Such, at any rate, is the opinion of the fishermen of Martha's Vineyard, who will tell you that the only proper way to catch eels is by use of a trap made and operated precisely after aboriginal methods.

The First Self-Propelled Vehicle Ever Constructed

THIS is the vehicle devised by the French inventive genius, Cugnot, and made for the French government in the year 1770. Cugnot's first steam automobile was made in 1769. It attained a speed of only two and a half miles an hour, on an ordinary road, carrying four persons. It was designed not for speed, but for heavy trucking—the transportation of artillery. It is particularly worthy of note that this practical steam-propelled vehicle was made in the year in which James Watt, in England, took out his first patent on the steam engine that was afterward to become famous. It will be recalled that Watt vigorously opposed the idea of the application of steam to the propulsion of vehicles (one of the strangest paradoxes in the history of science), and that the contest in which Stephenson's "Rocket" convinced the skeptics of the feasibility of steam locomotion took place just sixty years after Cugnot's demonstration of the same truth. Civilization progresses slowly—or not at all if the rank and file can prevent it. It is said that the French government did not even test Cugnot's vehicle, after it was officially ordered and actually constructed. This record puts to blush our own governmental record of waiting only five years before testing the Wright airplane. However, we are not quite outclassed, for we refused to consider the Maxim machine gun at all, until England had adopted it and knighted its American inventor.

Chimneys for Motor Cars

WHEN the automobile was first used in England about a century ago, the horseless vehicles were provided with chimneys, or smokestacks, similar to those used on the railway locomotives developed at the same time. This was natural enough, as both types of vehicles were propelled by steam, the

THE LATEST PASSENGER AUTOMOBILE
Gasoline-driven omnibus of 1932, carrying passengers from coast to coast in America

production of which called for the burning of relatively large quantities of coal or wood. The need of a chimney under such circumstances to carry the smoke above the heads of passengers and pedestrians, was obvious. As most of the early automobiles were in effect modified stage-coaches, the smokestack was a rather long and conspicuous affair.

Contemporary pictures show that automobiling threatened to become a craze among our forebears of that period. Imaginary views of London streets show a jumble of strange motor cars, far more varied in form than actual types of to-day; but one and all provided with the inevitable chimney, which is usually represented as discharging its offensive smoke into the faces of disgusted wayfarers.

Now it appears that the vision of the artists (based, to be sure, on observation of actual chimneyed automobiles) was in a sense prophetic; for carefully conducted experiments recently made have demonstrated that the automobile of to-day, notwithstanding its relative smokelessness, does vitiate the atmosphere and imperil the health, if not the immediate comfort, of the wayfarer. The conditions of our crowded city streets are more in accord with the conditions imagined by the cartoonists of a century ago than most of us realize.

A curious feature of the report summarizing the situation, is that it suggests danger not merely to occupants of cars, who breathe the fumes of cars in front of them, and to traffic policemen and pedestrians, but also to the occupants of office buildings, because the latter receive their chief air supply from the street level.

THE EARLIEST PASSENGER AUTOMOBILE
Steam-propelled omnibus of 1827, plying between London and Brighton, England.

A Topsy Turvy Train

THE traditional fact of putting the cart before the horse seems a mild performance in comparison with the project of putting the track of a railway above the cars.

Yet this is literally what is done in case of a certain railway in Germany, running from Barmen to Elberfeld. The picture of this unique railway (below) gives a clear idea of its construction.

What would ordinarily be called the roadbed is in this case a road-roof rather, and the cars are suspended beneath it.

Below the cars themselves there is nothing at all but air and—if you come far enough down—water, the railway being an elevated structure spanning, in some places, a canal.

THE NEWEST "RAIL PLANE"

OVERHEAD RAILROAD, BARMEN-ELBERFELD

The car, swung from above, seems at first glance to be navigating too much after the manner of an airplane.

But there is no adequate justification for such skepticism as to the stability and safety of the suspended railway.

It is a matter of relatively simple engineering to make the original structure strong enough to hold any weight to which it will be subjected; and an equally simple problem to provide against derailment of the overhead wheels.

Should an accident nevertheless occur, precipitating the cars to the earth, it does not appear that the passengers would necessarily be in a worse case than the victims of an accident on the American type of elevated railway.

Meantime the suspension railway has certain rather obvious advantages over the other type.

At the outset there is the matter of relatively cheap construction, chiefly conditioned on the fact that the line of cars is suspended from a single rail.

A single wheel fore and aft provides rolling equipment for each car—there being no restriction on the size of the wheels, as there obviously is in case of the conventional type of car.

The expensive ties that hold the rails of the ordinary road in parallel are, of course, not required for the monorail track.

Even if, to allow for traffic in both directions, two rails are laid, they are not necessarily connected by ties. They merely take the place of the "up-town" and "down-town" tracks of the familiar elevated railways of New York City.

The car pictured above at the right is also suspended from a rail overhead. It is moved, however, by an air-propeller, like an airplane.

The Once Famous Bone-shaker

NOTHING marvelous, surely, about an old velocipede! Not now, certainly. It is merely an obsolete pair of wheels, of ridiculous appearance. But in its day—and it was a relatively long day, of the nineteenth century—this was an invention that ranked high. It enabled a man to lengthen his stride, in effect, while conserving energy. And when some one thought of putting sprockets on the wheels and thus still further multiplying the effect, the "safety bicycle" became a vehicle that had astounding popularity, until superseded in our own day by the yet speedier automobile.

An intermediate stage was the bicycle with ridiculously high front wheel. To ride this seemed a feat of daring, yet the machine gained great popularity late in the nineteenth century—though nothing comparable to the vogue of the "safety."

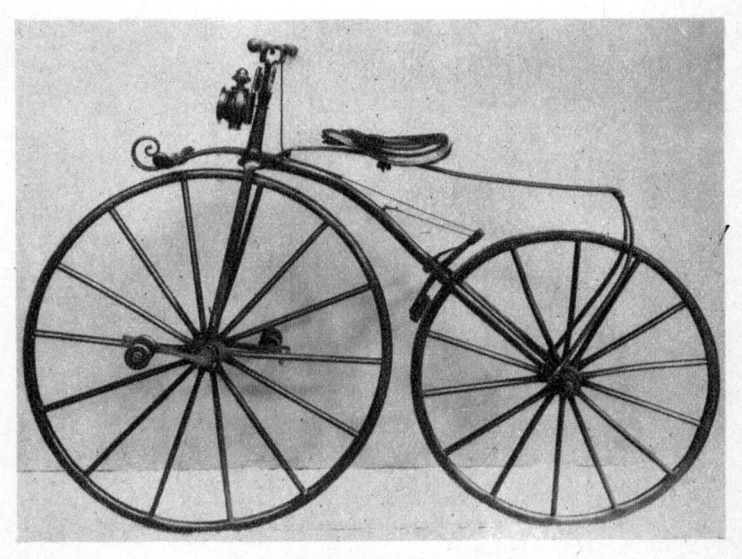

"BONE-SHAKER" BICYCLE

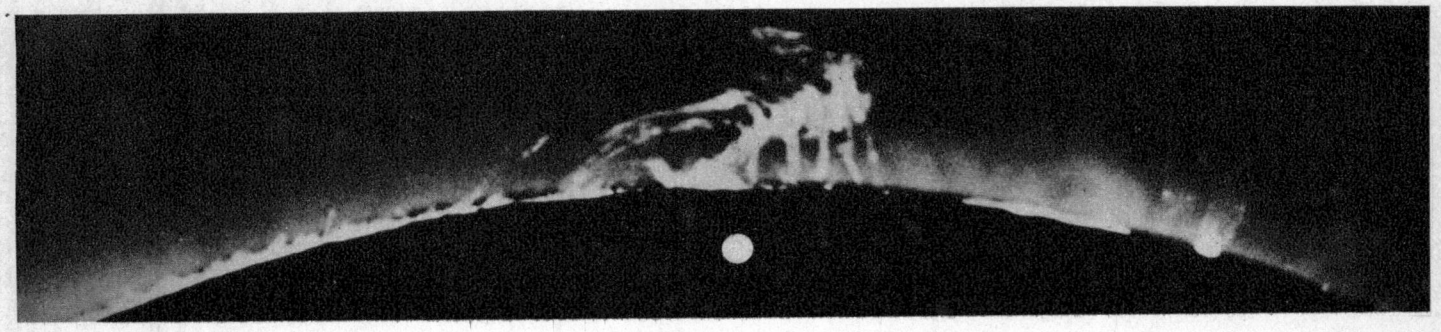

THE BOOK OF MARVELS

IF OUR EARTH VISITED THE SUN

If Our Earth Visited the Sun

IN the photograph, such a visit is being made. In view of the solar "prominences," which are great outbursts of flaming gases, it would appear to be a hazardous journey. If the earth were to drop into the sun, it would not make a splash of the slightest significance. Indeed, many hundred earths would need to be shoveled into the sun to make a dent as big as a well-developed sun spot. Much more than a million earths would be required to match the mass of the entire sun. From all of which it might appear that the question of the origin of the earth, as often debated by astronomers, cannot be of great importance, from the solar standpoint. If the earth was originally a "knot" in the skein of a spiral nebula, the knot surely need not have been a large one. Photo by Prof. Barnard, Yerkes Observatory, Chicago.

Testing the Sun's Chemical Composition

A SMALL telescope, with spectroscopic attachment, in the hands of Professor Charles A. Young, will test the chemical composition of the matter at the sun's rim, during the brief period when that body is hidden by the moon. The spectroscopic record consists of series of lines, which Fraunhofer and his successors proved to represent definite chemical elements. The feat of analyzing compounds situated in sun and stars, millions of miles away, is among the most bewildering of modern scientific achievements.

The Celestial Vagabond

THIS rather appropriate nickname has been given the comet, because of its apparent disregard of conventions in adopting size, plane, or contour of orbit. Some comets revolve about the sun without leaving the planetary system; others pass so far into outer space that it is doubtful whether they will ever return. But, of course, it is no longer in question that all comets obey the usual laws of motion, and gravitate about the sun precisely as planetary bodies would do under similar conditions. Comets are simply collections of meteoritic matter, "world-stuff" that has not been compacted into planetary masses. Their spectacular tails are regarded as illuminated particles driven off from the main structure by the pressure of the sun's rays of energy. In the photograph, the comet seems to be stationary and the stars in motion, because a somewhat prolonged exposure was necessary, during which the telescope followed the moving comet, and thus made the stationary stars seem to move.

PROF. CHARLES A. YOUNG

Celestial Ghosts

BY "celestial ghost" I mean, of course, the comet. Perhaps "planetary ghost" would be more appropriate, for the comets I have in mind are authentic members of the sun's family, even though they may be a trifle erratic in their orbital habits. But in any event, the "ghost" part needs no qualifications, for the comet is a spook if there ever was one.

The qualifications of a ghost, I take it, are opalescent visibility, by night only; total unsubstantiality, and the power to excite awe in the beholder.

In each respect the comet registers one hundred per cent. As to its ghostly appearance almost any one can testify.

Its tenuousness is vouched for by the astronomer, whose verdict is sustained by the evidence that the earth has occasionally passed through the very structure of one of the celestial apparitions without our so much as knowing it.

And as to capacity to inspire awe—who does not know that in all times until the most recent, the advent of a conspicuous member of the fraternity has been held to portend national or international disaster?

This is the penalty for being misunderstood, for the official record reveals the comet as being as harmless as every other ghost.

Its body, we are assured, consists merely of a cloud of tenuous fragments of world-stuff that has hitherto failed to find lodgment on a more substantial solar or planetary body.

And the amazing "tail," is nothing but a mist of electrons and dust particles so minute that they are driven off, literally, on the sunbeams.

That is why the tail follows the comet in orthodox fashion as the sun is approached, but precedes its parent body in paradoxical manner on the return journey.

BROOKS'S COMET

The Why and Wherefore of Sun-Spots

IF you can't find any other cause for a big terrestrial calamity, for example, an earthquake, blame it on a sun-spot. That seems to be about the way a good many people, including some astronomers, have reasoned for the past three hundred years or so.

No one could reasonably ask for a more satisfactory scapegoat. The sun-spot is more than ninety million miles away, and cannot possibly come any nearer. And it is so big that you could throw the entire world into a corner of it, as you would toss a small lump of coal into a furnace, without its being noticed at all.

Moreover, it appears to be demonstrated that there may be a connection between the appearance of sun-spots and the phenomenon known as a "magnetic storm" on the earth. If the sun-spot can affect the magnetic needle, why should it not cause tornadoes and earthquakes and the rest?

All of which is merely to say that the sun-spot is an anomalous phenomenon, of mysterious origin and of unknown influence.

Until Galileo's first telescope showed the existing spots, in 1610, it had been supposed that the sun's face is the most perfect of surfaces—that being the ancient Greek notion that had come to be accepted as an almost sacred article of faith.

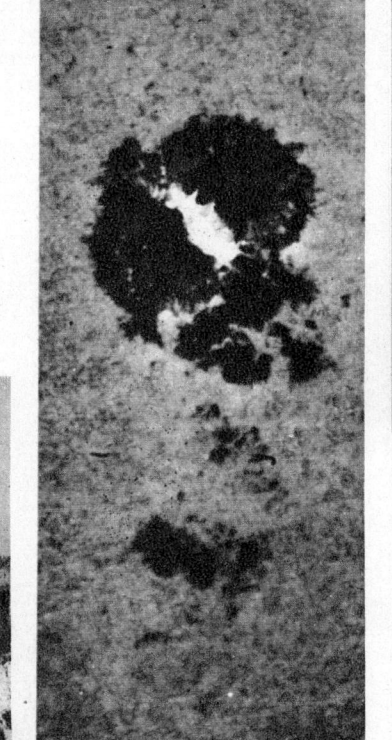

SUN-SPOTS

After that, sun-spots were studied, at first resentfully and then with interest; but very little came to be known about them until modern times, when the big telescopes, aided by photography and the spectroscope, revealed them as great vortices in the sun's gaseous surface. Just why they appear in greater numbers at intervals of eleven years remains a mystery.

Professor T. J. J. See, the Mare Island astronomer, believed that he had solved the mystery.

He believed that the spots are an after effect of the accelerated flow of the equatorial part of the sun's fluid surface caused by the precipitation thereon of great swarms of meteors detached from the cometary systems of the planets Jupiter and Saturn.

There is friction between the equatorial current and the more slowly revolving surfaces of the middle-latitude regions, resulting in disruptive effects that manifest themselves as "spots."

The periodicity of the sun-spot maxima is due, Professor See believed, to the successive conjunctions of the planets, occurring of necessity at regular intervals, and bringing swarms of meteors to destruction in the sun. And it is held that there is no alternative hypothesis that accounts for the observed facts. As yet this theory is not generally accepted.

Lava Needles in Yellowstone Park

THE "needles" are the eroded tops of veins of lava injected from the depths of the earth. The horizontal strata through which the lava (then in molten condition) was injected are of less resistant material. So part of their substance has worn away, under action of the elements, and the needle-like cones of lava remain. The view as a whole furnishes an impressive lesson in geology.

LAVA NEEDLES, YELLOWSTONE PARK

CAUGHT IN A WATERSPOUT

Caught in a Waterspout

THE waterspout is the marine equivalent of the "twister" tornado of the land. It is air violently whirling, which raises water as the land cyclone raises a twisting column of dust. Waterspouts are rare outside tropical regions, and not very often observed even there. They are naturally dreaded by seafarers, especially navigators of small craft.

The North Pole as a Way-Station

EVEN in these Einsteinian days, a straight line is still defined, I believe, as the shortest distance between two points. If the straight line is to be other than imaginary, it must obviously be drawn or laid out on a plane surface. A moment's reflection makes it clear that a line drawn along the surface of a globe cannot conform to the definition of a straight line. A straight line between London and New York, for example, does not follow the "level" surface of the ocean, but dives deep into the earth, emerging only at the termini.

You can illustrate this familiar truth very tangibly by letting an orange represent the earth, and puncturing it with a hat-pin, a knitting-needle, or any other slender instrument. You may also perform certain other experiments that will demonstrate another practical truth that is enormously important for navigators, with the import of which you may or may not be familiar. I have in mind the demonstration that a line drawn along a "great circle" is the shortest distance between two points on the earth's surface that a voyager can travel, since he cannot dive through the structure of the earth itself. Thus the short route between Europe and Japan would cross the polar region.

This is simple enough, but now comes the puzzling feature. One "great circle" is known to everyone as the equator. The parallels of latitude, as their name implies, are drawn parallel to the equator. You can demonstrate them by cutting your orange into successive slices of even thickness. Each successive slice shows a smaller circle of rind—for, of course, these are not great circles. All points on any given parallel are in the same east-and-west line. And yet the shortest traveling distance between any two such points would not be along the parallel.

If you were going by airplane to visit someone who lives a hundred miles directly east of you, you would gain time by starting out in a northeasterly direction, and you would never head straight east except for a moment just half way on the journey; the remainder of the trip being charted southeasterly.

GLACIER POINT, YOSEMITE PARK, CALIFORNIA

Glacier Point in the Yosemite National Park

IT would be hard to find a better example than this of the effect of a glacier in gouging the sides of the valley down which it flows. The sculpturing of almost perpendicular walls is a specialty of ice-action, under such conditions. The erosive effects of running water are no less significant in the end, but are produced less expeditiously, and result usually in more sloping valley-borders.

The Crater of Oblong Geyser

THE crater of this Yellowstone Geyser shows the deposit of salts that are left as the water evaporates. The material thus deposited was dissolved from the rocks in the depths of the earth by the hot water.

Mountains of Marble

THE dolomites of the Austrian Tyrol give their name to the region which they make famous. Dolomite is a limestone that has been heated till its constitution became partly crystalline, approaching the state of marble. The metamorphosis has not been complete enough to obliterate altogether the marks of original stratification. The present jagged mountain-forms of the dolomites are due, of course, to the action of the elements. When the strata were originally upheaved, scores of millions of years ago (according to recent chronological estimates), the land surface was more or less level, above the tops of the present dolomites. Few things in nature are more impressive and thought-provocative than such natural wonders as these.

CRATER OF OBLONG GEYSER

As It Looks to the Fish

AS you stand on an embankment at the water's edge and look off across the smooth surface of a pond, did it ever occur to you to ask yourself how things would look if you were just reversing conditions, and making your observations from the viewpoint of the fish?

I am not sure that anyone knew how the world really looks to the fish until Dr. Francis Ward, an English zoologist, constructed special apparatus for making photographs under water.

Dr. Ward proved that, in the main, the surface of the water from below is a mirror that reflects the water-bed and submerged objects.

Only a relatively small circle directly above the fish brings refracted light, and thus serves as a virtual window through which the fish may peer into a restricted portion of the air-world.

DOLOMITES

A Garden Valley in Utah

THE mountains that rise in the background have peculiar interest, as they show a succession of geological strata. The irregularities of erosion are due to the differing degrees of hardness of various rocks. The strata were formed in a sea bed, and the record remains of successive elevations and depressions. This type of mountain, carved from horizontal strata, is characteristic of some regions of the western United States. Wind, bearing sand, has a considerable share in the sculpturing. The elevation, without distortion, of such large areas is believed to be due, at least in part, to the pressure from below of the semi-molten matter beneath the crust; which in turn is squeezed back under the continent by the weight of the sedimentary matter deposited near the coast.

A GARDEN VALLEY IN UTAH

THE BOOK OF MARVELS

DEAD MAN SIPHON ON LOS ANGELES AQUEDUCT

A THREE-HORNED MONSTER

DIPLODOCUS

A Modern Aqueduct

AQUEDUCTS are a prime essential of all cities—ancient no less than modern. The inverted siphon in the Los Angeles aqueduct pipe here shown illustrates the modern method of carrying the water across uneven territory. In a closed tube, water, once started, flows up hill as readily as down; in a real siphon it even rises above its source.

A Three-Horned Monster

THIS strange beast is known as Triceratops, because of his triple horn. He was of gigantic size, but of vegetarian habit, and armored only for protection against some of his Dinosaur confreres that preferred to feed on flesh. The head with its shield was sometimes upward of eight feet in length—from which the size of the entire beast is seen to be prodigious. "There were giants in those days." According to the newest chronological estimates, the age of these great reptiles culminated about four hundred million years ago. Their fossilized horns, helmets, and bones are preserved in rocky strata that were originally mud-beds at the bottom of lakes or "flood plains" of their period.

Prehistoric Monster Called Diplodocus

THIS is one of the figures in the celebrated Hagenbach garden at Hamburg. The Diplodocus, known only by its fossil remains, dates from the Mesozoic Era, or Age of Reptiles. It was one of the largest of Dinosaurs; amphibious in habit; and a vegetarian.

To Alaska for Ivory

IF you were in quest of elephant trunks, about the last place in the world you would think of exploring would be Alaska. Yet it appears from a photograph issued by the U. S. Forest Service that ivory has been found in that unlikely field. The picture suggests that successful hunters are exhibiting the results of their prowess. One pair in particular of the gigantic tusks towering beside them could have been grown only by an elephantine creature of such dimensions as to make the largest African elephant seem a pigmy by comparison.

But the men who stand beside the remarkable exhibits are not hunters. They are miners, and their great ivory prizes were dug from the earth. The animals whose jaws these tusks once ornamented have been dead for thousands of years. The race to which they belonged has vanished from the earth—though the existing elephants are of closely related lineage.

The great prehistoric beasts have been christened Mammoths. They died so long ago that their bones have mostly been resolved to dust, the ivory tusks alone resisting the elements throughout the intervening years.

The race of prehistoric mammoths did not altogether perish, however, until the Arctic region had assumed something of its modern aspect; for the body of a mammoth was found in Siberia in the latter part of the 18th Century, embalmed in a block of ice. The flesh of the beast was so well preserved, after all those centuries, that dogs ate of it.

Frozen flesh is about as durable as ivory itself—so long as it remains frozen. The reason, of course, is that at freezing temperature bacteria that cause decomposition of organic tissues cannot develop.

For the preservation of the ivory tusks, not cold but dryness is essential. These Alaskan souvenirs are found in fairly good condition because they have been buried deep in the earth where water reached them seldom if at all.

Our picture shows a fine array of ivory-bearing walrus heads from Alaska. The walrus is the only present-day producer of ivory in the old home of the mammoth.

WALRUS HEADS

SEALS ON AN ICE CAKE

SHIPMENT OF AFRICAN IVORY

Life in the Sea

FAR up beyond the Arctic Circle big creatures like the musk-ox, the caribou, the polar bear, the white fox and the wolf thrive; and Stefansson found seal abundant far out in the Polar Sea, ensconced—air-breathers though they are—beneath vast sheets of ice that for weeks, or even months, may remain unbroken. The seals gnaw holes in the ice to get air; but their food supply is found in the sub-glacial waters. Stefansson, heading his sledges out into the unknown with scant equipment, virtually staked his life on the thesis that there is no northern limit to the habitat of the seal—and won. Other investigators, fortunately with less hazard, have shown that northern waters contain living creatures in unbelievable numbers. A few bucketfuls of the water, aggregating the weight of a man, may contain a population of minute organisms outnumbering the total human population of the United States. It is not unusual to find a living organism to each cubic millimetre of water.

THE BOOK OF MARVELS

He talks in the most matter-of-fact way about certain animals that commit "murder"—having no reference, of course, to the carnivorous beasts that normally secure their food by killing.

And in particular is it of interest to note Dr. Hornaday's estimate of the comparative intelligence and ability of certain conspicuous wild animals.

The estimate is no offhand guess, but a carefully tabulated statement taking into account ten different specific attributes—to wit: Hereditary knowledge, receptive faculties, original thought, memory, reason, receptivity in training, efficiency in execution, nervous energy, keenness of the senses, and use of the voice.

The highest degree of efficiency in each field is marked 100, making it possible for a superlative animal to pile up 1,000 points.

The highest aggregate actually attained is the chimpanzee's 925 points; the next highest is the 850 points attained by two wild animals, the orang-utan and the elephant, and by two domesticated animals, the horse and the dog.

Next below these we find the lion, the grizzly bear and the beaver, each with 725 points; then the red fox and brown bear

CHIMPANZEE SEWING

Animals with Brains

I HAVE just been reading Dr. William T. Hornaday's fascinating book on the minds and manners of wild animals. "Minds" and "manners"!

The book bristles with illustrations of the thinking power of individual animals; and as to manners—why, he has a chapter on the laws of the flocks and the herds that might not inaptly be characterized as an exposition of animal etiquette.

He shows that there are rules for normal behavior that the same animal never thinks of transgressing.

He shows, also, that there are individual animals, just as there are individual men, with criminal instincts or propensities.

STRANGE USE FOR AN ELEPHANT

TRAINING A LION CUB

A BEAR ON SKATES

CLIFF SWALLOWS AND THEIR MUD NESTS

(650), the gray wolf (625), the tiger and the white-tailed deer (each 575), and the gorilla, which ranks only as high as the coyote, each scoring 500 points.

A Decimal in Every Yard

THERE could not possibly be a better illustration of the power of tradition to dominate human activities than the fact that despite its practical superiority and scientific value it has proved impossible to introduce into this country the metric system as applied to weights and measures.

There are of course practical difficulties in the way of change of standard of measurement as applied to manufactured implements, but these difficulties would quickly be overcome if the popular sentiment could be aroused to the full appreciation of the merits of the metric system.

One difficulty is that many people, confused by unfamiliar names, fail to realize that the peculiarity of the metric system is merely its decimal notation. Our system of dollars, dimes, and cents, furnishes a perfect illustration. Everyone knows how convenient this is, as contrasted, for example, with the English system of pounds, shillings, and pence. Yet many people feel that it would be a hardship were they called upon to apply the simple and familiar dollars-and-cents method to commodities that we weigh and measure.

Of course a measure of hardship would be involved, at first. When one is accustomed to speak of yards and inches and pounds and ounces, a certain mental effort is required to substitute meters and kilograms and their decimal divisions. But, once the substitution has been made, the advantages are enormous. All the cumbersome tables that children memorize with such difficulty — "Two pints make one quart; four quarts, one gallon," and the like—could be promptly thrown into the discard—and the elementary fact that ten units of one order make a unit of the next order would serve as basis for all computations.

But until the average voter comes to understand that it is a matter that personally concerns him, we can hardly expect that anything effective will be accomplished in the way of giving up a cumbersome system that is obsolete in most other countries.

NEST OF THE WILSON THRUSH

A Birdland Mystery

IT is not alone the trees and flowers that give one cause for wonderment when one goes into the country in the spring. The birds can also supply an element of mystery. They, too, can set us asking questions that are hard to answer.

How, for example, did robin and bluebird and flicker know that March had come when there was nothing at all in the weather conditions to suggest the springtime? Quite evidently they kept track of the calendar and were guided by that rather than by weather conditions. But how did they do it?

And if the robin found it good and expedient to hurry back to us in March, why do the other thrushes, his cousins, delay their coming till May? By no chance do wood thrush and hermit thrush and veery put in appearance until some weeks after the sight of the robin has ceased to be a novelty; and when they do come they hold themselves aloof from the dooryard and orchard, seeking out the most primitive woodlands. If a Wilson thrush were to come familiarly about the dooryard and build his nest in the grapevine by the chimney as the robin does, we should think it not merely anomalous, but almost a violation of natural law.

But why should there be this difference in habits between birds that are so closely related?

It is no answer at all to say that it is the "nature" of robin and phœbe to come about the dooryard; whereas it is the "nature" of wood thrush and wood peewee to haunt the wilds. For in primeval times, before the white man came, all these birds must have been habitants of nature's wild garden.

Consider how very notable the change is in many cases. Here, for example, is the familiar barn swallow. It is well named, because it seldom places its nest now anywhere except on a rafter in the farmer's barn; yet obviously it could have found no such coign of vantage in the primeval days. Similarly the cliff swallow now plasters its mud nest under the eaves and the purple martin occupies a bird house or belfry.

Even more notable is the change of habit of the chimney swallow, which now invariably glues the framework of twigs to form its nest inside a chimney, giving no further thought to hollow trees.

And all this is more remarkable because for every species that has thus changed its nesting habits there are scores of species that have not changed at all.

A BATTLESHIP OF THE NINETEENTH CENTURY

A Battleship of the Nineteenth Century

AN amazing craft, certainly, is this great ship of the line *Marlborough*, of 131 guns, with engines of three thousand horsepower. It was just a wooden shell, of course, for in 1854 there was no such thing as an armored ship in existence. But it ranked as one of the most formidable instruments of destruction afloat. Scanning with modern eyes this photograph of the model in the South Kensington Museum, it is hard to realize that this floating tenement house was ever supposed to be a fighting mechanism. But all things are relative, and modern ordnance was as non-existent in 1854 as the armor plate it is designed to pierce. And then, if we wish to complete the picture, we may reflect that a bomb-dropping airplane would find this relatively small ship harder to hit than one of its twentieth-century successors—and that the effect of the bomb would be to send the armor-clad ship to the bottom rather more expeditiously than the wooden one. Perhaps there is not much to choose, then, between the craft, after all.

An Up-to-Date Battleship

THE airplane carrier is the only type of battleship that is likely to be of substantial use in the next big war. The armored monsters have been rendered obsolescent by the airship. The first airplane carrier, the U. S. S. *Langley*, was rebuilt from the old collier *Jupiter*, the first naval vessel to be equipped with the electric drive. Two aircraft carriers subsequently built from material originally planned for battle cruisers are much more formidable. Each of these is a craft 850 feet long, de-

AIRPLANE CARRIER *LEXINGTON*

signed to attain a speed of 33 knots (not far from 39 miles) an hour. Four electrically driven shafts will develop 180,000 horsepower — almost seven and a half times more than the propelling energy of the *Maryland*, which represents the navy's speediest existing type of ship.

But the new vessel is not a battleship in the old sense of the word. It carries no big turrets and gigantic guns. Its fighting equipment will consist of airplanes. The top deck is flat, for receiving and launching airships. The hold is a giant hangar for the storage of airships. The ship has a superb radio equipment, partly for the control of pilotless airships.

It will be able to send out airplanes without pilots but under absolute control, laden with bombs that can be launched against an enemy ship or coastwise city with more than the accuracy of cannon balls and with a deadliness of effect far exceeding that of the most terrific broadside ever fired by the sixteen-inch batteries of a dreadnaught.

AIRPLANE CARRIER *SARATOGA*

Bomb-Dropping Airplanes

IT is a fair presumption that the success of bomb-dropping tests against superannuated warships accounted in no small measure for the willingness of various nations to scrap formidable portions of their navies. To the candid observer it looks very much as if the airplane had made the big battleship obsolescent. In any event, the bomb-dropping plane must be reckoned with by all belligerent nations in future. We do not hear much talk about scrapping the battle planes.

On the contrary, we hear a great deal about the further development of the airplane as a warlike mechanism. In particular, we learn that new types of airplanes are being developed for the express purpose of carrying aerial torpedoes.

The same flying machine that can thus convey a half-ton load of human passengers can as readily convey a torpedo of corre-

MODERN CRUISERS

New but Obsolescent Fighting Ships

THE heavily armored battleship has always been a menacing rather than a performing engine of destruction. It has now become practically useless, except as an easy target for bomb-dropping airplanes. It serves in diplomatic circles, however, to make conversation, and to serve as a pawn in the international game of pretended disarmament.

The First Ironclads

THE fight between the *Monitor* (right) and the *Merrimac*, March 9, 1862. The result, although not absolutely decisive, was a virtual victory for the *Monitor*.

ARIZONA

sponding weight. And it has been amply demonstrated that a torpedo may be launched from the airplane up in cloudland, with deadly accuracy. The torpedo does not drop in a straight line but the combined forces of inertia and gravitation determine its parabolic course; and all that is necessary is to fly directly toward the object aimed at and to release the torpedo at a calculated moment.

It is impossible for a moving plane to drop anything straight downward. You are never in danger from an airplane if it is directly above you. It may sometime be a satisfaction to you to recall that fact when you chance to be in a crowd over which airplanes are maneuvering. The plane is a menace to you only while it is at a considerable distance, and headed directly toward you.

THE FIRST IRONCLADS

TUG OF WAR BETWEEN ELECTRIC AND STEAM LOCOMOTIVES. ELECTRICITY WON
Courtesy of the General Electric Co.

Water in Place of Coal

MAN could not travel very far along the path to civilization so long as the sweat of his brow was the chief measure of his working capacity. But he learned how to multiply his powers of accomplishment. He made the ox and horse work for him; he shackled wind and water; and ultimately he dug from the earth coal, and bade it perform labors veritably herculean.

The most recent addition to man's list of co-workers is electricity. It had the great merit of extreme transportability. You had but to furnish it a highway of wire, and it would of its own accord follow the track you had made. But part of the current was frittered away in transit, and beyond a rather limited distance this power carrier could not be sent economically. If electric power plants were erected beside the waterfalls, as at Niagara, their range of operations was limited to an area of not many miles.

Then came the discovery that by using high voltages, the current could be forced along a prescribed channel, with negligible loss. And that discovery gave sure augury of a new industrial era. At once there was new interest in waterfalls, and it became evident that coal was outrivaled.

Consider, for example, the case of the Province of Ontario, Canada, which has neither coal beds nor oil fields, and which therefore, after the exhaustion of the forests, was under necessity of importing every ounce of fuel it used. What chance of industrial advance along manufacturing lines had such a region?

The authorities awakened to realization of the power going to waste in numerous waterways; and in particular to the harnessable colossus, Niagara. Various private companies undertook the work of harnessing the cataract, and by 1924, 380 municipalities received current for electric light and power, to the aggregate amount of 700,000 horsepower, distributed from twenty-one plants over a network of wire aggregating more than 3,000 miles of high-tension lines alone. Ontario has to-day the best-developed hydroelectric system on the Western Hemisphere.

The Extraction of Nitrogen from the Air

IN the Norwegian plant shown below, the extraction of nitrogen from the air, and its combination with alkaline earths to make commercial fertilizers, is accomplished. When the method was first devised, early in the present century, it was accounted a marvelous feat. Theretofore it had been impossible to make chemical use of the inexhaustible supply of nitrogen in the atmosphere. Other methods of extraction were soon developed, and the nitrogen-extraction industry assumed great importance. Had it not been possible to secure nitrogen-supplies for the making of explosives in this way, the Central Powers could hardly have carried on for four years of World War. The peace-time uses of nitrogen are numberless. The artificial product is by way of supplanting "Chili nitrate," from the guano beds.

A NORWEGIAN PLANT IN WHICH AIR IS CONVERTED INTO FERTILIZER

Tesla's Problem

THE distinguished electrician, Nikola Tesla, has labored so long on the problem of conveying power without wires or other man-made conductors that this may be said to be distinctively his problem. Perhaps no other electrician of recognized standing regards the project as feasible. But for Tesla, it is an ideal surely attainable; perhaps even now attained, at least in principle.

Thanks to the availability of the high-frequency current which Tesla himself had so large a share in developing, it is easy to send energy into the ether from a wire-system, as is done in radio broadcasting or other radio transmission. But the energy thus liberated radiates in all directions, or at least in all lateral directions, over the surface of the globe. Radio receivers by the thousands, located here, there and everywhere, may each pick up a little of it, and the rest is ultimately absorbed, presumably by the earth itself.

NIKOLA TESLA IN HIS LABORATORY

THE AUTOMATIC CONTROL OF HEAT

A Magic Heat Regulator

IF one of our forebears of the pre-electric era could have been shown a thermometer hanging in a small case on the wall, and told that by adjusting a pointer beneath the instrument, the temperature of the room would be automatically regulated, he would doubtless have thought you either downright mad or a plain, every-day liar. But when a test of the apparatus had proved your claim valid, it would have become clear to the witness that you were practising magic. No alternative explanation would have presented itself.

Yet the "magic" heat regulator above postulated is in reality the simplest and least mysterious of instruments. It really does the thing suggested; you have but to tell it what temperature you wish maintained in the room, and within reasonable limits it will see that your orders are carried out. You can even tell it—with the aid of an attached clock dial—at what hour tomorrow morning you wish to have the heat turned on, and you may go to bed confident that the thing is as good as done. That, if you please, is magical; yet the way the thing is done is so simple that a child can understand it.

The principle involved is merely the perfectly familiar one that heated bodies expand, and that the same bodies on cooling contract again. In the thermometer case, then, is a little piece of metal whose big name, "thermostat," need not disguise the fact that all it does is to lengthen a bit when the temperature rises, and in so doing break an electric circuit. If the temperature falls a degree or so, the thermostat shortens and closes the electric circuit. Add that the electric circuit links with an electric motor that operates the furnace-draft or a steam-pipe valve, and we have the whole story—a story of scientific magic, if you will, but with no hint of occult mystery.

The Heart of Our Planet

IT is held to be pretty clearly established that the central mass of the earth—the physical heart of our planet—is composed of iron, constituting an irregular sphere about 4,200 miles in diameter; with the reservation, however, that the core may possibly be of platinum or gold instead of baser metal. That seems an important reservation, until we reflect that iron, gold and platinum have equal value—or lack of value—when located eighteen hundred miles beneath the surface of the earth.

WEIGHING THE WORLD

CLIFF PALACE, MESA VERDE NATIONAL PARK

The Cliff-Dweller Palace

THIS is the largest of the pre-Columbian Cliff Dwellings in the Mesa Verde National Park, in southwestern Colorado. The structure, built into the side of a precipice, after the manner of dwellings of this extraordinary type, is 300 feet long, and contained about 200 rooms. It is the largest known example of this unique type of prehistoric American architecture. Though called a "palace," it was presumably the abode of a large number of people—in effect, a cliff city, rather than a house. Mystery surrounds the questions of origin, ethnic relations, and fate of the builders of these unique structures.

The Egyptian Sphinx and Pyramids

THIS ancient monument has excited the wonder of everyone who has seen it, for more than three thousand years. No one has adequately explained the purpose that actuated its builders. The neighboring pyramids are understood as the tombs of kings. But the Sphinx is the symbol of mystery. In the background is one of the pyramids—considered even more wonderful, by the ancients, than the Sphinx.

The Parthenon at Athens

STANDING on the Acropolis, and still marvelously preserved, this is one of the most famous monuments of antiquity, and among the most beautiful structures of any age. It dates from the middle of the fifth century, B. C. Equally beautiful is a Greek temple at Paestum, Italy, perhaps older than the Parthenon.

THE EGYPTIAN SPHINX

PARTHENON AT ATHENS

Bas-Relief Sculptures from Assyria-Babylonia

THESE marvelous sculptures, quite unknown to the modern world until about the middle of the nineteenth century, have given us new insight into the life of antiquity. Note the details of working-methods revealed in the picture of the transportation of the Colossal Winged Bull. The other figure shows a scene in the Temple of the Sun God of Sippara.

The Cold-Heat Paradox

THE energy that comes to us from the sun through this ocean of ether-filled space comes in the form of ether-waves, traveling at the speed of 186,000 miles per second. The space through which they travel is commonly spoken of as being at the absolute zero of temperature—which is another way of saying, at no temperature at all. In the nature of the case, empty space—or ether-filled space, which comes to the same thing in this connection—can have no temperature. Where matter is not, there can be no heat.

But whereas all this is technically correct, and certainly worth thinking about, the important fact remains that the ethereal energy-waves that come from the sun have the power to set up motion among the particles of matter when they impinge upon it on arriving at the earth, and thus they generate heat, even if they themselves are heatless.

You have but to stand for a few moments in direct sunlight, to demonstrate that fact to your entire satisfaction. And if you choose to insist that the heat which you feel has come from the sun, most people will let your claim go unchallenged. Nevertheless, it is interesting to reflect that out there in space, directly between you and the sun, in the very path of the seemingly hot sunbeams, there is absolute coldness.

An interesting demonstration of this fact—involving, indeed, at least by implication, the principles of radiant heat above outlined—was made at the Electrical Exposition in New York in illustrating the action of a reflector of radiant heat called a simplex sunbowl.

The concave copper reflector, with an electric heater as its

(Upper Figure) TRANSPORTATION OF COLOSSAL WINGED BULL
(Lower Figure) TABLET FROM THE TEMPLE OF THE SUN GOD OF SIPPARA

focus, sent out a shaft of ether waves that brought a warm glow to the body of anyone who stood within their range; and the feeling of warmth was in nowise modified when a big blower, like an overgrown electric fan, was set in motion, causing a miniature hurricane directly across the path of the heat-beams.

Meantime, the moving air of the imitation hurricane neither deflected the heat-engendering ether waves nor was appreciably warmed by them. Elementary physics, to be sure, but a demonstration that caused wonderment to hosts of people who themselves participated in the experiment.

Egyptian Temples

EGYPTIAN civilization was at its apex before European civilization became significant. The subsequent Greek civilization borrowed largely from Egypt. Compare this picture with that of the Greek Parthenon.

EGYPTIAN TEMPLES

Pillars of Faith

THE region where most of these ancient pillars stand is known now as Brittany. The monuments themselves are of two principal types, known respectively as menhirs and dolmens. "Menhir" means merely "long stone," and "dolmen" means "table stone."

Menhirs, whether large or small, are long in proportion to their breadth; and the flat stone supported by other stones to constitute a dolmen has a rough resemblance to a table.

When the menhirs are arranged in files, with military precision, the group is given the name of "alinement." Sometimes a circle or square of menhirs constitutes a "cromlech," which may terminate an alinement or surround a tumulus.

Cleopatra's Needle

THIS name is commonly applied to all Egyptian obelisks; or at least to those that have been transported to other countries. The obelisks date from periods far antecedent to the time of Cleopatra. Together with the Sphinx and the pyramids, they rank among the chief marvels of ancient skill in the hewing of stone and the handling of objects of enormous weight.

CLEOPATRA'S NEEDLE, CENTRAL PARK, NEW YORK

PILLARS OF FAITH. PREHISTORIC DOLMENS AT STONEHENGE, ENGLAND

The Astounding Oil Industry

THE "mineral" oil industry, developed from nothing in a half century, is among the most amazing phenomena of any age. It furnishes a panorama of marvels, from the scene of the picturesque oil fields (a) where the crude product is secured; through the stages of transportation by tube (b) or train (c) to the refining plant without (d) or within (e), where the crude oil is "cracked" to make many grades of compounds, of which gasoline is nowadays the most familiar. Harking back to the first oil well which, about the middle of the nineteenth century, produced twenty barrels per day of oil that found a doubtful market; and reflecting that each year now the American motorist spends as much for gasoline as it cost to run the United States Government any three years before the War—one is overwhelmed with wonder. Assuredly we are living in an age that is "different." And when we reflect that without the product of the oil wells we should have neither motor cars nor airplanes, it would appear that ours might well be called the age of gasoline.

THE FIRST OIL WELL

The First Oil Well

THE first oil well, property of Col. E. H. Drake, is said to have been sunk between May 20 and August 27, 1859. It was 69½ feet deep, and produced twenty barrels of oil per day for an entire year. This well was a world-marvel at the time, and the possibilities of the future oil industry did not begin to be appreciated till long afterward.

RECOVERING GASOLINE

Irrigating with Ice

THE idea of efficiency which is supposed to be so dominant in business offices nowadays finds occasional application on the farm as well. Witness, for example, the use of mechanical power in many capacities, from the hauling of tractors and the filling of silos to the milking of cows. A multitude of devices prove that farming is no longer the wasteful process that it once was.

But all previous efforts of conservation of material would be outdone if the ingenious idea of Elton F. Reid, of Waco, Texas, could be put into practical effect.

His plan calls for such conservation of water as perhaps no one hitherto ever dreamed of. His suggestion involves the use of a rifle-like mechanism to fire a series of bullets into the soil. Each bullet is to be directed into the root-system of an individual plant or cluster of plants—say a hill of corn.

These bullets are made of ice. The machine that discharges the bullets is adjusted on a tractor that has a refrigerator system that makes a series of ice slugs to keep the weapon perpetually loaded like a machine gun.

When the ice slug has found lodgment amid the roots of the plant, it will of course, melt presently, and supply water for nourishment of the plant. The water being supplied in this concentrated form, just where it is needed, none of it will be wasted.

FILLING OIL CARS AT PLANT

Two of the World's Most Famous Cathedrals

ST. PETER'S, at Rome, designed by Bramante and Michelangelo, and St. Paul's at London, the work of Sir Christopher Wren—each a triumph of architecture; one of the sixteenth century, the other of the eighteenth.

ST. PAUL'S CATHEDRAL, LONDON

ST. PETER'S, ROME

New Automatics for Life-Taking and Life-Saving

NOT quite without surprize, and certainly not without humiliation, one learns that it has been thought desirable to devote human time and ingenuity to the invention of a new type of machine gun. One might have supposed that engines of destruction of this type had been perfected to the nth degree, having in mind the weapon that sowed such havoc in France.

But it appears that there is no such thing as the last word in a mechanical device; and of course common sense forbids even the most optimistic to affirm that the machine gun is an anachronism in present-day civilization. So it is permissible to look with interest, if not quite without regret, on the deadly new weapon that General John T. Thompson has invented.

The gun will deliver single shots, or will pour forth bullets at the rate of a hundred a minute, at will of the operator. Tests made at Tenafly, N. J., in the presence of army and police officials from various States, are said to have been convincing.

One of the greatest merits of the gun is that it weighs only nine and a half pounds. It is thus readily portable. Indeed, it has something of the appearance of an elongated pistol. In an emergency, it might be added to the equipment of patrolman or motor cop. And in war time —but why dwell on an abhorrent topic?

Let us consider for a moment rather, by way of antidote, the development of another new automatic machine which sends out projectiles of a quite different type. I refer to the device for making medicinal tablets which has been placed on exhibition in the Arts and Industries Building of the United States National Museum.

The tablet industry has grown to enormous proportions in recent years, yet for the most part it has remained a hand industry. Using a perforated metal plate as a multiple mold, the hand operator could produce a large number of tablets in a day. But the new machine, operated merely by throwing an electric switch, turns out the tablets at the rate of from one hundred to three hundred per minute—outrivaling the machine gun.

A Typical Modern Oil Forest

THE status of the present-day oil industry needs no exposition. The origin of the oil that flows from these wells in almost unbelievable quantities is not generally understood, and even geologists do not fully agree on the point. The prevailing opinion is that the oil represents the residuum of the bodies of countless minute animal organisms, of a comparatively late geological period. The idea of vegetable origin has been largely abandoned. Natural oil, though a carbon compound, is thus held to be in nowise related to coal, which, as is well known, is of vegetable origin.

OIL WELLS IN TEXAS

POURING INGOTS

The Steel Mill Wonderland

A STEEL mill is a wonderland of wonderlands to every visiting novice. It remains a wonderland, no matter how often visited. The photographs show typical aspects of the successive stages through which material that was once iron ore passes in the course of its transmutation into the finished product. Difference in the quality of steel may be due to the different processes or to the raw materials used and the care with which the process in question is conducted.

The World as a Whispering Gallery

IT appears that a present-day broadcasting station spreads its program of words and music impartially across a territory aggregating—as a simple calculation reveals—something like twenty million square miles.

Nor does this represent by any means the limit of possible transmission, if it were thought desirable to utilize greater power. Doubtless it would be feasible to-day to establish a station, let us say, in the Panama Canal Zone that could be heard from Alaska to Patagonia. And to-morrow, when it becomes expedient to put the new hundred-kilowatt and thousand-kilowatt tubes in harness we may expect the transmitting range to be so extended as to bring not merely a hemisphere, but the entire world into the same whispering gallery.

From that hour, national boundaries will weaken. The spirit of internationalism will grow. It cannot be otherwise. Radio by itself will be a tremendous force making for cosmopolitanism of view. The airplane will be its efficient co-worker.

These two eliminators of time and space, demolishing artificial barriers of race and creed, and ignoring the geographical barriers that hitherto seemed formidable, will carry forward the work of unification begun by printing press and steam engine and telegraph and telephone.

When statesmen at Washington, London and Tokyo can hold joint conferences, with the rest of the world listening not merely to the words but to the very intonations of the voices, a new diplomatic era will be at hand. That will be "open diplomacy" indeed. The homely old admonition to think twice before speaking will take on new force for anyone who realizes that fifty million or a hundred million people may be listening.

A Big Locomotive

WHY is a big engine any greater marvel than a little engine? Was not Stephenson's little four-ton "Rocket" a greater marvel than any other steam-driven locomotive can ever be?

There is cogency in such questions, with their implied answers. They need not be challenged. The first steam locomotives—including Stephenson's—were greater marvels than any of their successors, because they demonstrated the possibility of the practical application of steam power to vehicular locomotion. When that had been demonstrated, the big engines were sure to follow.

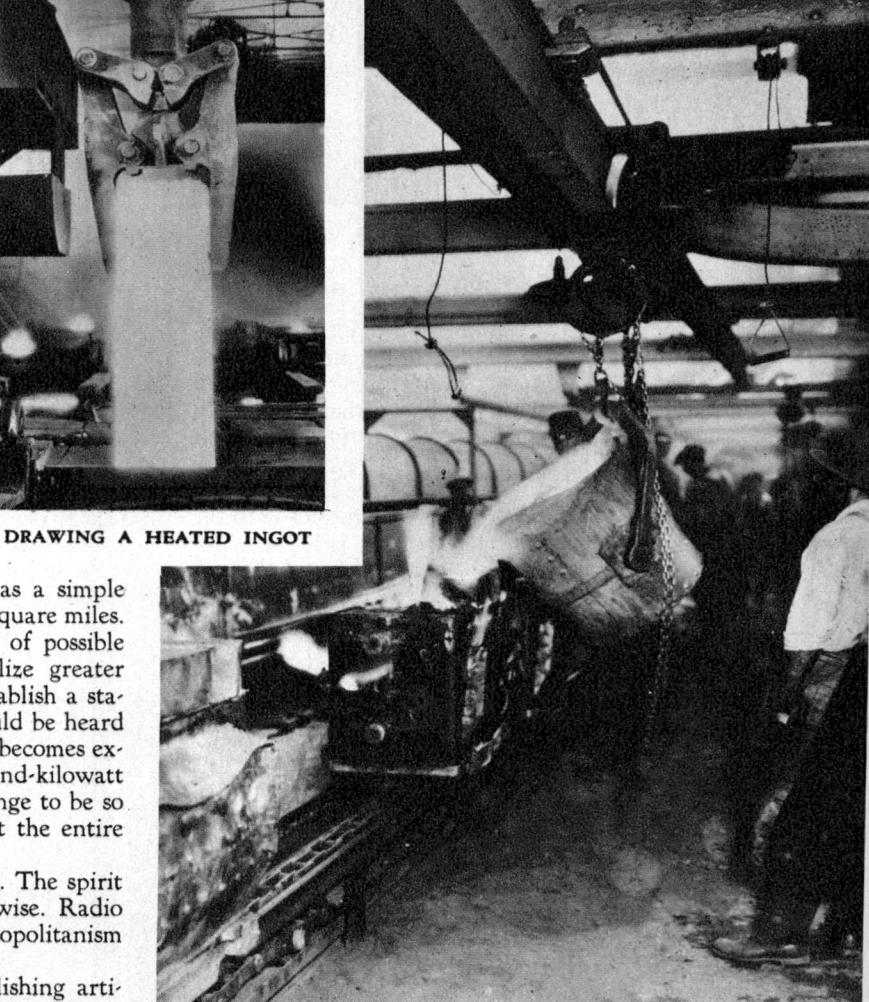

DRAWING A HEATED INGOT

POURING MOLTEN METAL INTO MOLDS

BOILER OF A BIG LOCOMOTIVE

And yet the fact remains that we do wonder and feel a sense of astonishment—not to say awe—whenever we are confronted with a new example of a familiar mechanism made of bigger size than any previous one. Mere size does count in determining our estimate of the apparatus. A very big machine does seem more marvelous than a moderate sized one.

It has always been so. Because of mere size, certain structures were counted "Wonders of the World" in antiquity, and their fame has lasted through the centuries. We are not told that the Colossus at Rhodes was especially beautiful. It was big. The Sphinx is big. The Pyramids are big. That is why we marvel at them. Any sculptor could carve a sphinx. Any fair artizan could build a pyramid. But the gigantic Sphinx. The monster Pyramid? How could anyone make such colossal structures? That is the real point. It is size that makes the "Wonders" wonderful.

So I make no apology for standing in wonder before the great engine built by the American Locomotive Company. I recall Stephenson's marvelous "Rocket," as I have seen it in the South Kensington Museum, with boiler six feet long and about three feet in diameter—a structure which, when its tank was filled with water, weighed about four tons.

Then by way of contrast I note that the boiler of the modern locomotive is more than eight feet in diameter, and that its low pressure cylinders would hold the "Rocket's" boiler, with plenty of room to spare. I note the twenty driving wheels, each nearly five feet in diameter; the ninety-seven-foot wheelbase of engine and tender; the total weight of 463½ tons; the water capacity of 13,000 gallons; the total heating surface of 8,608 square feet; the tractive power of 176,600 pounds, plus 147,200 pounds for the compound engines. And though the figures for the most part convey vague meanings, they combine to spell the clear word "Marvelous!"

A GIANT AT NIGHT

Why Do Radio Waves Hug the Earth?

BACK in the year 1901, when young Marconi, fresh from his success in sending wireless signals across the English Channel, proposed the audacious scheme of signaling across the Atlantic, he was ridiculed by scientists and laymen alike.

Did not everyone know that, the earth being round, there is a great bulge equivalent to a mountain 200 miles or so high between Europe and America? And was it not well understood that the wireless waves, being electromagnetic vibrations in the ether, closely akin to light waves, must travel in straight lines, and, therefore, would go shooting off into space on a tangent? If you had an antenna pole 200 miles high you might intercept transatlantic signals. Otherwise the thing could not be done.

Yet presently the thing was done. And it was found that the antenna poles need not stretch up hundreds of feet even, let alone miles. Indeed, it was ultimately proved that an antenna may even be buried several feet under ground, or laid at the bottom of a lake or river, and still receive radio messages sent from hundreds of miles away.

It has even been demonstrated that radio messages may be received at the Antipodes—half way round the world, with a bulging mountain 4,000 miles high between sending and receiving stations.

Obviously, then, the radio waves that carry these messages hug the earth, instead of rushing off into space on tangential lines. But how is the anomaly to be explained?

As to this scientists have never been agreed. One theory has it that there is a layer of atmosphere a good many miles above the earth's surface that has its atoms "ionized" by the action of electrons coming from the sun, and that this so-called "Heaviside layer" reflects the radio waves just as a mirror reflects light.

CHEMIST ANALYZING CREAM

The Pasteurization of Milk

MILK is the universal food, and the process that makes it wholesome after shipment to cities is one of the most important applications of scientific discovery of modern times. Millions of infant lives are saved by commercial application of the discovery that heat destroys the bacterial germs of disease. The photographs show (a) the glass-lined tanks in which the milk is heated to about 145 degrees Fahrenheit; (b) a chemist analyzing cream; and (c) the automatic bottling and capping of the finished product.

Milk and Vitamins

UNQUESTIONABLY pasteurization safeguards the public health. But there are few unmixed blessings in this life, and it is at least an open question whether the milk thus improved in one respect by heating is not at the same time injured in another respect. The question has been many times raised in recent years whether heating the milk does not destroy or greatly reduce its vitamin content. And vitamins are so important that they have been not inaptly referred to as constituting the "growth principle."

Light and Life

THE word "photosynthesis," frequently used by the biologist, has not made its way into common usage. Yet it refers to what, from the human standpoint, may be regarded as the most fundamentally important of all chemical phenomena—the building up of organic compounds out of inorganic matter, under the influence of light. The green coloring matter of plants, called chlorophyl, is the only agent

BOTTLING AND CAPPING

known to be capable of accomplishing this miracle; and chlorophyl can work only in the light. Hence the word "photosynthesis," equivalent to "light-combining," or "building done under stimulus of light."

There is no other kind of building done in the world that is so important as this, for without it there could be no living thing. The process consists primarily of the union of carbonic acid gas (secured by the plant from surrounding air or water) with water, to form what are called carbohydrates (starch, sugars), and it is followed by the union of these compounds with nitrogen, to form protein, or protoplasm, which is the basal "life-substance." No animal can accomplish the original combination; nor can any plant, except it be supplied with the necromantic chlorophyl; and if you keep the chlorophyl in total darkness, it is powerless.

That is why most plants thrive in the sunlight and languish in the shade, and why no plants, except possibly parasitic ones, are found in totally dark caves, or in the depths of the ocean beyond the reach of the sun's "photosynthetic" rays.

Comprehensive tests have shown that the plant-building power of the sun may be supplemented notably by the use of electric light during part of the night.

PASTEURIZING MILK

THE BOOK OF MARVELS

Aseptic Surgery

THE present familiarity of the method should not lead us to forget that the results of antiseptic and aseptic surgery, commonplaces of to-day, were miraculous half a century ago.

The Great Moment in American History

DR. WILLIAM T. G. MORTON administered ether for the first operation under anesthesia at the Boston General

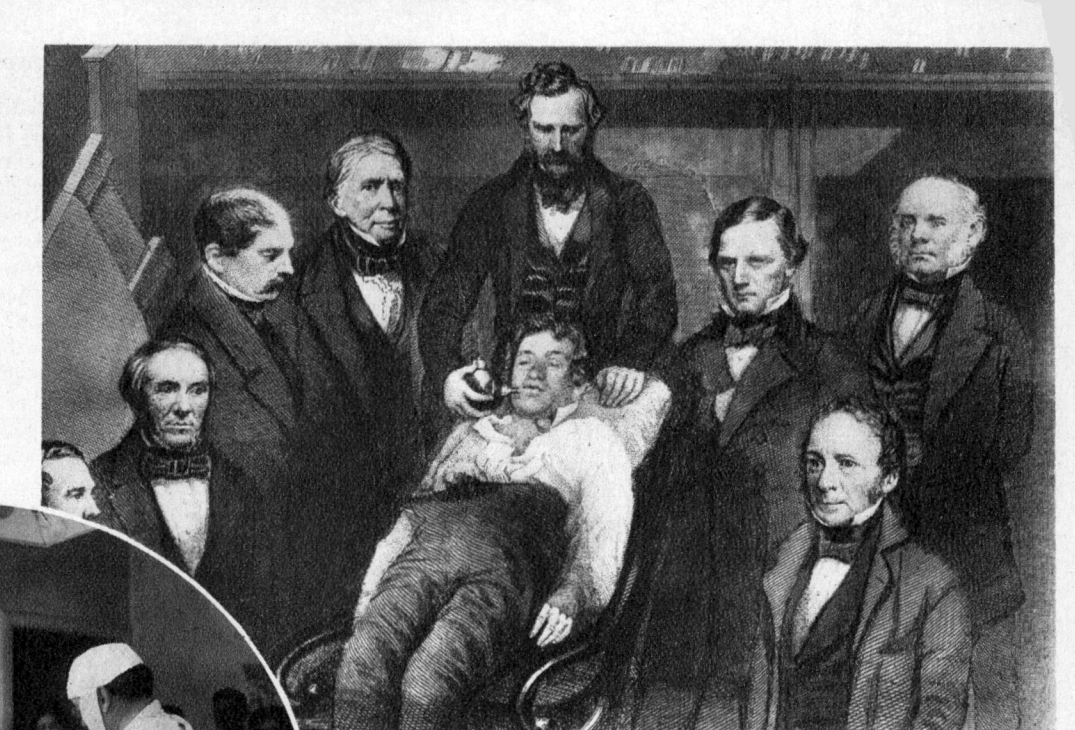

DR. WILLIAM MORTON ADMINISTERING ETHER

Hospital. Earlier use of ether had been made by Dr. Crawford Long, of Georgia, but this demonstration, made by Morton, gave anesthesia to the world. This perhaps was the greatest boon ever conferred on humanity by one man. The Boston demonstration must be adjudged the most important incident in American history—and among the very greatest in world history.

Combating Diphtheria

FEW accomplishments of modern medicine give occasion for greater or more justifiable pride than the success attained in combating the deadly germ known as the Klebs-Loeffler bacillus, the microbe responsible for the malady, once appallingly fatal, and still feared by every mother of young children, known as diphtheria. Medicine, to be sure, has not banished the malady, but much has been done to reduce it to a subordinate place in the mortality tables, and there are few if any virulent maladies of which there is better promise of ultimate complete conquest.

SAFETY IN SURGERY

The story of the development of the specific antitoxin, inaugurating the new method of serumtherapy, is well known. In recent years most parents have heard of the Schick test, which shows whether or not a child is susceptible to diphtheria, and of the toxin-antitoxin inoculations that give immunity. With these weapons in hand, it becomes in a sense a matter of choice as to whether or not any child shall be permitted to have diphtheria —or would be so did not the elements of human carelessness and lack of foresight enter so largely into this, as into every other social problem.

TAKING ANTITOXIN FROM A HORSE

THE BOOK OF MARVELS

Astronomy as a Hobby

IN northwestern Iowa, near the little town of Washta, lives (or did live when last I heard of him) an old farmer, Frank Carrington, a rugged fellow in his seventies, whose hobby is star-gazing; or, to be quite accurate, planet-gazing. He has built a very practical observatory as an adjunct to his farmhouse.

Carrington's observatory, built with his own hands, represents an outlay of seventy-five dollars. If you were to view it from a little distance, you would probably mistake it for an abbreviated silo, or possibly an ice-house. But on closer inspection you would find that the round brick structure has a revolving roof, delicately adjusted.

For purposes of study of our neighbor planets, and of the sun and moon, such an amateur observatory as this may serve as well as a far more elaborate and costly establishment. And the man who can devote the leisure hours of the long winter evenings to cruising along the canals of Mars, inspecting the wonderful rings of Saturn, or wandering through the valleys of the moon is living a very different life, indeed, from that which the imagination of the car window inspector pictures. He is voyaging in far-off wonder-worlds.

Of course, not all Iowa farmers are amateur astronomers in their leisure hours. Observatories are not as common as silos. There may not be another establishment quite comparable to Mr. Carrington's in the entire Mississippi Valley. But the number of amateur star-gazers in the aggregate is large, and there is no other group of individuals who have a more fascinating or a more spirit-exalting hobby. Mr. Carrington's example may well be emulated by anyone who cares to broaden his mental horizon by personally touring the whole universe.

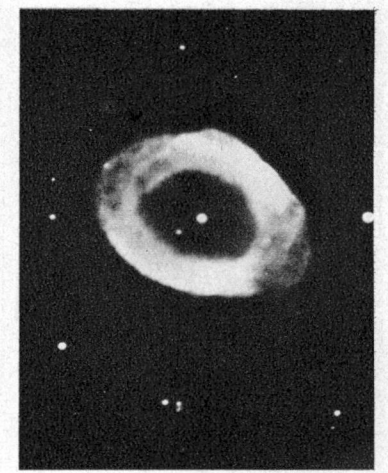

MODERN TELESCOPE

RING NEBULA

The Great Reflecting Telescope at Mount Wilson Observatory

THE sixty-inch reflector was for many years the most powerful reflecting telescope operating anywhere in the world. The broken line shows the comparative size of the one-hundred inch reflector which supersedes the other as the world's most effective telescope. Reflecting telescopes were invented by Sir Isaac Newton, but first used effectively by Sir William Herschel, toward the close of the eighteenth century. A six-foot reflector was made by Lord Rosse toward the middle of the nineteenth century, but this was by no means so effective an instrument as even the smaller of the Mount Wilson instruments.

The Pock-Marked Moon

TO inspect a photograph of the moon made at the focus of a big modern telescope is the next thing to paying a visit to the moon itself. The pock marks are craters of all sizes, often with borders raised to mountain-like height. What caused these craters? That is matter of controversy. Perhaps the best guess is that they mark the impact of meteorites, which have splashed up the moon-stuff about the spots into which they plunged—as a pebble splashes a little mud-crater of similar appearance. The moon has no atmosphere, and no water; so the craters are permanent.

THE MOON IN "CLOSE-UP"

A Marvelous Telescopic Ring

THE ring nebula is one of the outstanding telescopic wonders. Not only because of its appearance, which is remarkable enough, but because no one can very definitely say what that appearance indicates, as to the constitution of the nebula, or its past history or future prospects. As to these matters, one guess is about as good as another. Our picture is from a Mount Wilson observatory photo.

Measuring a Star

DR. PEASE, at the Mount Wilson Observatory, using the Michelson Interferometer, with the aid of which the miracle is performed of measuring the diameter of a star—an incredible performance, even in this age of scientific wizardry.

MICHELSON INTERFEROMETER

OWL NEBULA

How Measure a Star?

NO one needs to be told that to the naked eyes the brightest star appears only as a point of light.

It is to many people surprizing, however, to be assured that in the focus of the very largest telescope, the same thing is true.

Yet the fact is that the better the telescope, the smaller and more sharply outlined even the most vivid star appears. A needlepoint of light, and nothing more.

How, then, is it possible that the diameter of a star can be measured? Until recently it was not possible with any apparatus that man had been able to devise.

But now the thing is done, in the case of a few of the largest and relatively nearest stars, with the aid of the great 100-inch reflector—the largest telescope ever made—at the Mount Wilson Observatory.

The instrument that is used in connection with the great telescope to make the enigmatic feat possible is called an "Interferometer."

It is the invention of the late Albert Michelson, the distinguished physicist of the University of Chicago. It consists essentially of an apparatus twenty feet long, carrying a pair of small sliding mirrors, adjusted across the upper end of the telescope tube.

These mirrors reflect beams of light from the star that is to be measured in such wise that they are brought, after a second reflection, to the big mirror of the telescope, and thence focused and re-reflected and ultimately examined with an objective that magnifies the image several thousand diameters.

Meantime, the two beams of light thus brought to a focus have been split into their spectral lines, and a fringe visible through the lens is formed by interference, on the principle of the formation of a rainbow.

But as the little mirrors in the interferometer are moved further apart, the time comes, if the test is to succeed, when the two sets of light waves are in harmony and the fringe disappears.

A mathematical calculation based on the measured distance between the little mirrors and the known length of light waves gives the data for the final calculation.

The Owl Nebula

THIS is one of the oddest of celestial bodies. All nebulae are more or less puzzling, astronomical opinions having differed at various times as to whether some of them were actually nebulous, or only very distant groups of stellar bodies. It is still in dispute as to whether some nebulae may not be "island universes" lying far outside our galactic system. It is in doubt, also, as to whether spiral nebulae, which cluster in enormous numbers about the galactic poles, are actually receding from us at enormous speed, or have their spectra modified by the condition of their substance, or by the intervention of cosmic matter in space. The round planetary nebula here shown has been less the subject of conjecture, partly because of its relative rarity, and partly because no very plausible hypothesis in explanation of its uniform surface and seeming solidarity seems to have been presented.

YOSEMITE NATIONAL PARK

Tenaya Canyon in the Yosemite National Park

THE foreground rocks show typical effects of former glaciation. Boulders seen lower down toward the valley are other evidences that an ice sheet once covered this region. The Yosemite glaciers were local, far removed from the great ice-cap of the renowned "Glacial Epoch," which covered the northern part of North America and Europe. But the characteristic effects of glaciation, in rounding exposed rock surfaces and in transporting boulders, are everywhere the same.

Morning Glory Spring

THIS hot spring in Yellowstone National Park owes its name to the beautifully tinted incrustation about its borders from deposit of mineral brought up dissolved in the crystal-clear hot water. The photograph, by Haynes of St. Paul, is reproduced by courtesy of the National Park Service.

Arrowrock Dam at Boise, Idaho

THIS extraordinary dam was built in 1915. It is 349 feet high, and 1,100 feet long. It cost $4,328,000, and the capacity of the reservoir it controls is more than ninety-one *billion* gallons. The potential value of this water, in terms of future

GIANT MONOLITH, COLORADO

The Giant Monolith of Red Canyons Park

THIS colossal natural statue, near Canyon City, Colorado, is weirdly suggestive of a figure of Prometheus Bound, as Rodin might have conceived it in one of his Balzacian moods. Nature will have her little jests, and nowhere more amusingly than in the rock-sculptures of the Rocky Mountain region. This Giant Monolith comes very near to being her masterpiece. A fantastic conception, indeed, to leave this detached figure, heroically erect despite the bonds, and with upturned face, while removing every trace of all the matter that once encompassed it. In a sense, the figure was pre-formed in the original plateau of rock—as a sculptor's future statue is pre-formed in the marble as he conceives it—else it would not now remain. But by what chance did the skull of the future giant have exceptional hardness and resistance to erosion? It is easy to conjure fantasies about such a phenomenon. And in all soberness, the figure embodies a whole volume of geological lore.

MORNING GLORY SPRING, YELLOWSTONE NATIONAL PARK

A Water-Made Mountain

THIS so-called Mound Terrace in Yellowstone National Park, at the seat of the Mammoth Hot Springs, has obviously been built, in part at least, of mineral salts deposited when the water that flowed from the springs evaporated. The photograph clearly shows the stalactites festooned about the slopes, and piled into foamy masses. Of the many wonders of the Yellowstone, this is by no means the least marvelous. We think of running water chiefly as an eroding agent. Here we observe that on occasion it can serve in a constructive capacity instead.

DAM AT BOISE, IDAHO

MOUND TERRACE, YELLOWSTONE NATIONAL PARK

Great Falls at Yellowstone Park

WHEN an original "faulting" of rocky strata has furnished a precipice over which water can flow, the falling water tends to keep the precipice in being, and even to make it deeper, though gradually moving it up stream. This is because the water gains eroding power with the distance it drops, and therefore tends to erode the lower part of the precipice more than the upper part. Ultimately, the projecting upper part breaks away, re-establishing the perpendicular. As this process continues, age after age, the waterfall moves up-stream, leaving a carved-out valley to mark its line of march. The observed rate of erosion (very slow, of course), coupled with measurement of the length of the valley, furnish data for time-estimates, helping to reveal the age of the geologic periods.

GREAT FALLS, YELLOWSTONE NATIONAL PARK

When Midnight Is High Noon

IF you had risen early to enjoy the sunrise from the upper deck of a ship that had passed through the Panama Canal and was now cruising up the Pacific coast, you might be surprized to be told that the radio operator had just received an authentic signal indicating that the exact time was midnight, and that another signal gave the exact time as twelve o'clock noon.

That you should be observing the six o'clock sunrise at midnight and at noon simultaneously must certainly seem to you a bit Alice-in-Wonderlandish. Yet such an experience really implies nothing at variance with the normal and orderly sequence of events so far as natural phenomena associated with the lapse of time are concerned, and nothing mystifying except in the sense in which all radio phenomena are mystifying.

The explanation is simply that the first time-signal came from the radio station at Honolulu, correctly stating that the local time was twelve o'clock, midnight; whereas the second signal, received a few minutes later, came from Nauen, Germany, and stated with equal veracity and scientific accuracy that the local time was high noon. In each case the radio waves brought the signal with the delay of only a small fraction of a second (they go more than seven times round the world in the full second), and as Nauen and Honolulu are located on opposite sides of the world, with about 171 degrees of longitude between them, their conceptions as to when it is day and when night quite naturally differ. Nor will the emphatic statement of either one or of both of them serve in the least to shake your confidence, fortified by observation of your watch and the rising sun, that the time is really about six in the morning.

A SWAN-NECKED SAURIAN

When Reptiles Reigned

IN the Age of Reptiles there were notable tribes of aquatic or amphibian monsters, whose legs had become flappers, and whose necks were extended to swan-like proportions. The long necks doubtless enabled them to feed in deep water, or to lie in shallows and raise their heads above the surface for air. The so-called Plesiosaurus was typical, but there were many minor variations of form, as if nature were experimenting. Eventually all reptiles of this type became extinct, as mammalian life developed; but only after many millions of years of dominance. According to the chronology of my Biography of Mother Earth, the Mesozoic Era, or Age of Reptiles, lasted 450,000,000 years.

The Oldest Man

A HUMAN skull from the Tertiary! That was the really exciting news on the front page of the papers the other day. Think of it—from the Tertiary!

But where, you ask, is the Tertiary, and why should the finding of human remains there prove exciting? Did no one ever explore the Tertiary till now?

The answer is that the Tertiary has been often enough explored in our day, and thousands of relics found there, but that hitherto all these relics have been the fossil remains of animals lower in the scale of evolution than man—the Tertiary being, in short, the geological epoch otherwise known as the Age of Mammals.

In the Tertiary, the gigantic reptiles that had dominated the situation in the preceding age suffered a decline of fortunes, most of them becoming extinct in due course; whereas mammals were in the ascendant, finally developing the types that are still in existence.

With the exception of the very highest of mammals—man himself. Of him, no trace after all these years of searching since geology became a science.

But now comes the report that down in Patagonia a skull assuredly human, though exceedingly primitive, has been exhumed from strata accredited to the Tertiary age. Hence the excitement.

Every day there are thousands of persons searching the archives of libraries in the hope of tracing their pedigrees even a single generation farther back. And here is an ancestor that all of us may claim, who dates, let us say, from the year 1,000,000 B. C.

He is our great-great-great (repeated perhaps thirty thousand times) grandfather. Merely to name him thus, in expression of the relationship, would require column after column of space.

It makes him seem a long way off, to be sure. But are not ancestors in general prized directly as the square of their distance? Ask the searchers of the genealogical records.

It remains to be said that in the present case, as so often when pedigrees are in question, the records may require a little more authenticating. Is the new find really from the Tertiary? That is the question that every ethnologist will ask.

So it may be at least provisionally assumed that the nose is broken of old Pithecanthropus erectus, the ape-man of Java, who has hitherto been conceded first place on the scroll of man's ancestry.

The Neanderthal man, of the Old Stone Age, comes to seem almost a modern.

NEANDERTHAL MAN, OLD STONE AGE

PITHECANTHROPUS, AS DR. McGREGOR CONCEIVES HIM

A Deep-Sea Mystery Solved

TIME out of mind, the origin of the eels has been a mystery. These strange, snake-like fish never breed, even though sojourning year after year in the waters that constitute their natural habitat. No one has known just how the species is propagated.

At last the mystery has been solved, and the eel is revealed as a creature with the strangest of life-histories. The secret was discovered by Danish naturalists who have been making deep-sea soundings far out in the ocean. They find that the breeding place of all the common eels, of both Europe and America, is the sea bottom, a mile or more in depth, in the neighborhood of the Bermuda Islands.

Geological History in Montana

THIS photograph, taken from a summit above Swiftcurrent Pass, in Glacier National Park, tells a fascinating story of more or less recent happenings in this region—if interpreted in geological terms. We see the record, first, of the deposit of sediment that became rocky strata in ancient sea beds. These were upheaved, to form a monster plateau, which was gradually worn down by erosion to near sea level; constituting then a so-called "peneplain." After a time, a new upheaval occurred, carrying the surface of the peneplain high into the air, to form a plateau thousands of feet above sea level. On this plateau, the elements worked, as always, wearing away the less resistant parts, and carrying off the detritus by way of rivulets and rivers. More resistant portions of the surface here and there were left, at about the same level, to form the table mountains and peaks shown in the picture. The process of sculpturing is, of course, still going on; perhaps as fast as at any time in the past. The entire period of which record is here revealed may be perhaps a billion years; but the main work of chiseling out the mountain-forms most in evidence is recent—perhaps accomplished mostly within the past hundred million years.

IN GLACIER NATIONAL PARK

Winning Against Odds

MY Connecticut farm is located about an hour from New York City as the crow flies—when in a hurry.

But as you wander across its rugged acres you would never suspect that you were within ten times that distance of a great center of human population.

Your walk might lead you into woodlands suggestive rather (unless you are well versed in the signs of second-growth timber) of a primeval wilderness.

The presence of white-tailed deer, red foxes and raccoons in the woods will oblige you to concede that it is wild territory, even if not a veritable wilderness.

To me the presence of the deer in particular is a source of perennial astonishment.

These creatures, be it understood, are out-and-out wildings. They scarcely come in contact with man—perhaps for the most part are hardly aware of his existence.

But very different, indeed, is the case of certain other wildings of the furry tribe, which have voluntarily left the woodlands and come to reside in neighborly touch with the human invaders; making their homes in meadow and pasture and barnyard.

I refer to the chipmunk, the squirrel, the weasel, the skunk, and in particular, the ubiquitous woodchuck.

Here are creatures relatively small in size, to be sure, but conspicuous; creatures that make themselves obnoxious to man; creatures not merely unprotected by game-laws, but upon the heads of some of which bounties have been placed in times gone by.

Generation after generation, every man's hand has been against them. They have been shot, trapped, poisoned, harassed by dogs—and in many regions to-day they are as abundant as they can well have been in the time of the first settlers.

WOODCHUCKS

CHIPMUNKS

BURBANK'S SHASTA DAISY AND ONE OF ITS PROGENITORS

The Shasta Daisy

THE production of this large and very beautiful flower, by combining strains of European, American, and Japanese daisies, was one of the greatest triumphs of Luther Burbank as a plant-breeder. Many varieties were developed, all characterized by pearly whiteness of petal.

The Oldest Living Things in the World

THE "Big Tree" (Sequoia gigantea) of California is probably entitled to this distinction. Not only are the individual trees of relatively enormous age (upward of three thousand years), but they have the distinction also of being descended from ancestors from which they do not greatly differ that thrived perhaps a hundred million years ago, in the Tertiary period.

About Heliotropism

IN the course of his seemingly endless series of experiments with the little insect called a fruit fly, Professor Thomas Hunt Morgan, of Columbia University, has been able to juggle with hereditary characters almost at will, and to note the curious combinations of characters, physical and functional, that are transmitted sometimes only to offspring of a single sex.

He tells, for example, of producing a race of tan-colored flies that have lost the "positive heliotropism" that is so marked a feature in their normal ancestors. Being interpreted, this means that the flies no longer move instinctively toward the light when disturbed. And this new trait proves to be what is called a sex-linked character in inheritance; for when tan-colored females are bred to normal wild males, their offspring will be found to comprise normal (gray) females and tan-colored males; and if the entire brood is placed in a dark receptacle and then disturbed, all the females will fly to the light, the males remaining behind—the grays and the browns being thus automatically

BIG TREE GROVE, CALIFORNIA

separated. That certainly is a very odd illustration of crossed (from mother to son) and sex-linked heredity.

Just why the tan color, in case of this fly, should be associated with loss of the normal tendency to fly to the light, it would be difficult to say. Everyone has seen plants turn toward the light, and the moth's flight to the candle is proverbial. Sundry biologists, notably Dr. Jacques Loeb and his associates, studied the phenomenon in many phases, and Dr. Loeb contended for, and apparently demonstrated, the mechanical nature of the response; but the physio-chemical explanations hitherto attempted can hardly be said to be altogether satisfying. However, it is something to be assured that the impulse that directs the insect toward the light is not voluntarily suicidal, but more closely comparable to the "impulse" that impels an unsupported body to fall toward the earth.

The "Day-by-Day" Formula

THE "day-by-day" slogan popular a few years ago was among the happiest of its kind. Its greatest merit lies in its universal applicability. Its application to physical health-seeking is only incidental, however important. It applies with equal cogency to practically every business activity. For in effect it is but a felicitous variant of the old copybook maxim: "I'll try always succeeds."

REDWOOD GROVE, CALIFORNIA

Let me illustrate this patent truth with an out-of-the-way example. I refer to the work of the late Luther Burbank, the plant "wizard" of Santa Rosa. If ever there was a line of achievement that demonstrated the value of the "day-by-day" formula, it is his.

Consider, for instance, the task of developing a spineless cactus. Few tasks could be less inviting. The cactus revels in spines, and spines are not pleasant things to handle. In particular is this true of the spinelets of the baby cactus. These are often too small to be seen, but not to be felt. Mr. Burbank's hands became furry with them, as day by day he went about his task of selecting the more promising subjects among the thousands of seedlings.

The experimenter himself has recorded that at times his courage faltered. The task

CACTUS FIELD IN BLOOM

BURBANK'S SPINELESS CACTUS

seemed disagreeable, even painful, beyond human endurance. But in his subconscious mind there rang constantly the equivalent of the "day-by-day" slogan; and if at times he faltered, at least he never stopped.

And day by day his cactus beds got better and better. Or if not day by day; at least year by year. The tireless selection of the less and less spiny ones for propagation led progressively to more and more tangible results; until at last the totally spineless cactus —with leaf smooth as the palm of your hand —was an actuality.

And the "day-by-day" slogan, singing itself in the heart of the experimenter if not on his tongue, was the real secret of his ultimate success.

TREE USED BY WOODPECKER TO STORE ACORNS

Has a Tree Personality?

A TREE grown from a seed and having roots and trunk and branches that get larger for a term of years and then die might be thought of as having an individual personality. It is a living thing, and apparently a unit structure. Yet it is possible to juggle with the personality of this individual in a curious way.

For example, you may cut a twig from the tree, and graft this twig on the branch of another tree; and the transplanted twig will live and flourish under favorable conditions, and appear to become a component part of the tree upon which it has been grafted. But the transplanted twig, and all the branches that may grow from it, will maintain the characteristics of the original tree, although gaining nourishment from a tree of quite different origin.

So there you have a very pretty puzzle. Is the apple tree that grows in your dooryard an individual personality, a unit structure? Or is it only part of an individual—one member of a complex body with thousands of other members in various parts of the world?

I venture to predict that the more you think about that problem the more puzzling it will become.

The Thriftiest Bird

THE bird that makes the holes, notably in the bark of the yellow pine, and stores an acorn in each hole, is the California woodpecker. The U. S. Forest Service authorities, who supply this photograph, do not approve of this habit, as it is not beneficial to the tree. But the woodpecker is indifferent to criticism. Storing food for the winter is an exceedingly unusual habit in birdland. The nuthatch stores sunflower seeds in the crevices of bark, but there is no third bird known to me that emulates the example of mice, chipmunks, and squirrels in making provision for a future snowy day. The woodpecker must be especially credited, because he personally makes the receptacle in which food is stored—an almost perfect storehouse, from the bird's standpoint, whatever the forester may think of it.

MODERN SUBMARINE

The Latest Type of Submarine Boat and Earlier Types

THE submarine boat will perhaps have a certain utility in warfare after surface warships have been completely abandoned. The newest use for submarines is in Arctic exploration. A submarine that carries an airplane is the newest marvel of the species—and perhaps the most notable advance towards greater destructive efficiency in marine warfare of recent years. It is a British development.

Science and Sex

THE science of our time is perpetually warning us that the word "impossible" should be used very charily. In the day of X-ray and radium and airplane and radio, the seemingly impossible has become the commonplace. We must be prepared for any miracle, and accept it with a shrug of the shoulders when it comes. Naturally, then, there was very little excitement created by the announcement before the American Society of Zoologists that an adult female pigeon had been observed to change into a male. Time was when such an announcement would have caused at least a lifting of the eyebrows.

The observer who made the report is Dr. Oscar Biddle, of the Carnegie Station for Experimental Evolution at Cold Spring Harbor, Long Island, and he presents evidence that is quite unequivocal. Moreover, the observer did not hesitate to theorize a little to the effect that it now becomes wholly probable that "all hereditary characteristics of every human being and of every organism are capable of reversal and of modification and that the accomplishment of this merely awaits the definitely directed efforts of investigators in this branch of science." To say that is to suggest something a little out of the ordinary, even in this age of miracles.

The suggestion is fortified by the statement that years of investigation have proved that the sex of the pigeon can be changed in the embryonic or egg stage, coupled with observation of the reversal of sex in the adult bird just referred to; the change of the latter, it may be added, being associated with a tubercular infection.

Dr. Biddle refers to the observed change of sex of an adult bird (and he adds "or animal") as a rare occurrence, but not as being without precedent. And, in fact, there is record of a fowl over in Scotland that was quite as much an innovator in the feminist movement as the Long Island pigeon. This fowl, as reported by F. A. E. Crew, came to the Animal Breeding Research Department of the University of Edinburgh with the unequivocal history of having raised several broods of her own chickens. Until

U. S. S. *BEAVER*, TENDER OF SUBMARINES

SUBMARINE EMERGING

about three years old she was a typical hen in appearance, habits and egg-laying capacity.

Then she had stopped laying and begun to crow. Presently she began to develop typical characteristics of the male, including large comb, spurs and "cocky" feathers. Her instincts were reversed also, and the following season, under rigid observation at the research station, "she" became the unequivocal father of two chicks, the mother being a hen of ordinary proclivities.

Photograph by Underwood & Underwood
BRITISH SUBMARINE AIRPLANE CARRIER

DEEP-SEA DIVERS ASCENDING

A Benign Sea Monster

THERE are strange creatures galore at the bottom of the sea—creatures that through ages of adaptation have become fitted to live only at depths where light scarcely penetrates, and where the pressure is so enormous that the life would be instantly crushed out of any fish, for example, that should attempt to dive there suddenly from near the surface.

Nor can the deep-sea fish make the opposite journey with impunity. The air incorporated in their blood and tissues is so compressed that it may expand with almost explosive energy and suddenness if the fish is hooked and hauled quickly to the surface. Gradual transition is necessary if any creature from the depths is to be brought up uninjured.

Formerly it was questioned, even in scientific circles, whether a dead body, or even the hull of a sunken ship, would ever reach the bottom of the ocean, the suggestion being made that at a certain depth the pressure would become great enough to sustain even the heaviest object.

The fallacy of such an argument was apparent, however, when it was reflected that water presses in all directions.

No doubt a body that is not much heavier than water settles slowly in the depths, and compressible bodies are doubtless compacted to greatly reduced dimensions; but the final resting place is at the bottom.

When we say that a creature is "strange," we mean merely that it is different in appearance or habit from creatures to which we are accustomed.

No doubt we humans look as odd to the aquarium fishes as they look to us.

But fishes and men alike will agree as to the "strangeness" of a newly designed sea monster that is about to invade the depths.

To outward appearance it is a sort of headless giant, with distorted arms and legs, and with great goggles of eyes staring from its truncated torso.

Investigation will reveal, however, that this is a very harmless type of monster. It is, in reality, a novel form of diving suit, and it is designed to permit the man who will occupy and animate it to descend to a depth of a thousand feet or so, with the object of recovering treasure from sunken ships —even, perhaps, including the *Lusitania*.

The Amphibious Vehicle

THE old puzzle about the zebra— is it a white animal with black stripes or a black animal with white stripes?—comes to mind as one considers

TO DIVE FOR SPONGES

siders the newest type of pleasure vehicle: Is it a motor-car that takes to the water on occasion or a motor-boat that sometimes comes out on land? And apparently, as in the case of the striped animal, you may suit yourself about choosing an answer.

Names aside, the new amphibious vehicle perhaps represents a type that has possibilities of gaining genuine popularity.

The particular specimen shown in the photographs that come to hand from Berlin is, to be sure, a rather crude affair, distinctly of the home-made order.

It progresses along the ground like a motor-car, and it enters the water and progresses there like a boat.

And that at least establishes the viability of the idea of a combined land-and-water vehicle. The commercial manufacturer will do the rest.

"In Times of Peace"

JUST what should a nation do in times of peace? In the matter of warlike activities I mean, of course. The familiar old maxim presented above in abbreviated form supplies the traditional answer.

No one needs to be told what are the missing words. But neither does anyone need to be told that it is a maxim that has often been disregarded, in this country in particular, in the past. The story of the unpreparedness of 1917 has not yet been quite forgotten, even in official circles.

That is why it is possible to-day to arouse an interest that could not have been developed in the year 1913 in certain gas wells down in Texas containing a small percentage of helium, an element originally discovered in the sun (with the aid of the spectroscope) and observed to be abundant there and in certain types of stars, but not hitherto known to exist on the earth except in infinitesimal quantities.

Helium is just an inert, light, colorless, odorless gas that unites with nothing, and a few years ago apparently had no commercial possibilities. Someone did, indeed, suggest that it might be used to fill balloons, if enough of it could be secured, inasmuch as it is the lightest known gas next to hydrogen. But why bother about that, so long as hydrogen is cheap and abundant?

Then came the war, and the failure of the much-heralded Zeppelin for one cause only—the inflammability of its hydrogen-filled body. And almost overnight "helium" became a magic word.

Helium-filled dirigibles, it was obvious, might be war-engines of tremendous importance. Presently it was rumored that an unexpected new source of helium had been found in the Texas gas wells. The non-inflammable gas could be isolated cheaply and in quantity. Eureka!

That discovery probably did much to bring the war to a sudden termination. The helium wells had served their purpose. There was danger that they would be forgotten. But persistent effort has kept them within official purview and it may be hoped that the helium will not be wasted.

The Turbine Engine

THE turbine engine, invented by Parsons, acts on the principle of a multitude of small pushes, applied to series of minute blades, so adjusted that a portion of steam, in escaping from the cylinder, passes over one series after another. Rotary motion is thus achieved directly, instead of indirectly by an outside mechanism, as in the ordinary steam engine. The same basic principle is used in the turbine water wheel. The rotating propeller of a boat or an airplane may be said to use the principle in reverse. In one case, moving steam or water grips and pushes the obliquely set blade; in the other, the blade rotates and pushes the water or air. This rotor principle was early conceived, but its practical application was long delayed.

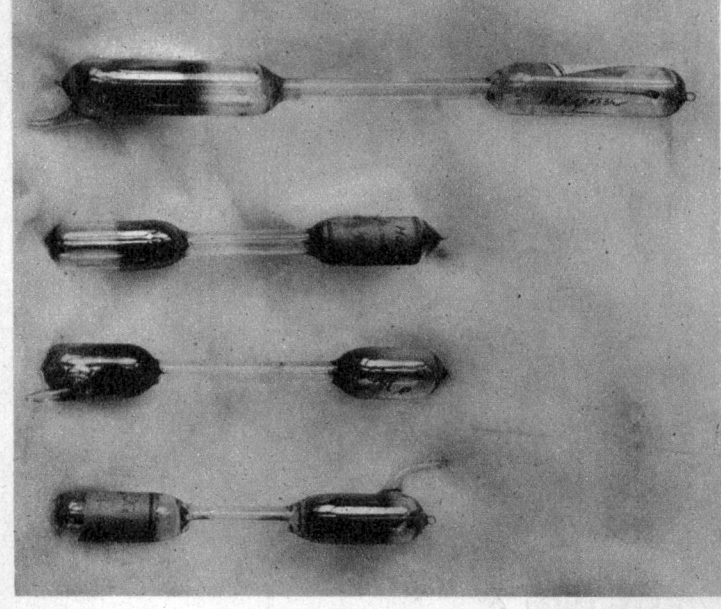

SIR WILLIAM RAMSAY'S TUBES OF INERT ATMOSPHERIC GASES

PARSONS'S HIGH SPEED TURBINE

Radium from the Desert

THIS is Paradox Valley, Colorado — appropriately named, since this seemingly inhospitable region is the seat of the quarries where the mineral is found from which radium is extracted in commercial quantities. The mineral ore is shipped to New Jersey, where the elaborate process of extraction and concentration is conducted.

RADIUM MINES

The Panama Canal

IN the ballot of the *Scientific American*, to determine what were considered the greatest marvels of the modern world, the Panama Canal was allotted eighth place. As an engineering feat, it has hardly been surpassed. Rather paradoxically, it ranks even higher as a triumph of preventive medicine; for it was here that General Gorgas demonstrated the possibility of conquering malaria and yellow fever by destroying the mosquitos that carry the germs of these maladies. The region was transformed from a pest-hole, where white men could hardly live, to a health zone. Our illustration shows a ship passing through the locks that are a feature of the Canal made necessary by the use of the high-level lake of the Chagres River.

GATUN LOCKS, PANAMA CANAL

SHIP PASSING THROUGH CANAL LOCK

Patrician Elements

CHEMICAL elements are like human beings: some are of democratic habit, mixing freely with their fellows whenever opportunity offers, while others are inclined to hold aloof, with patrician arrogance, mingling little or not at all with other elements.

The constituents of the atmosphere furnish extreme examples; oxygen is a bourgeois element, the best of mixers, combining with anything and everything that will meet it half way. What we call fire is merely the evidence of oxygen combining eagerly with an element—usually carbon or a carbon compound—that greets it eagerly. What we call rust is the evidence of oxygen combining slowly with molecules of iron. And every time we draw a breath, it is to permit oxygen to enter the lungs and thence the blood stream, that it may make combinations in our tissues lacking which life itself would not continue.

But very different is the habit of that other prominent constituent of the atmosphere, nitrogen. This also bathes the inflammable tissue, rubs shoulders, however unwillingly, with the iron molecule, and perforce enters the lungs with every breath; but such enforced physical contact leads to no chemical result. Not an atom of the atmospheric nitrogen combines directly with the inflammable carbon or the rustable iron or the living tissues of the body. There is, to be sure, a small increment of nitrogen in the living cell, but it gets there by an indirect route.

The true aristocrats of the atmosphere, however, are certain other elements, spoken of as the "rare gases of the atmosphere." These include several elements whose names have never become familiar to the general public, and whose existence was unknown until the early part of our own century, when Lord Rayleigh and Sir William Ramsay discovered them. They are called argon, xenon, neon and krypton, and each is an elemental substance, despite its lack of chemical activity. Associated with them is another element of equal aloofness, named helium. This one alone of the patrician family has become known, at least by hearsay, to the man in the street.

Helium got its name into the newspapers because it was found mixed (but not chemically combined) with natural illuminating gases in such quantities that it could be collected and used to fill balloons, thereby giving promise of a revolution in aviation. Its removal is accomplished by cooling the gases with liquefied oxygen till everything but the helium is liquefied.

A word as to the way in which helium itself and the other patrician gases of the atmosphere are tested by the chemist. Ordinary methods of combining with other elements obviously are not available. But there remains spectrum analysis, accomplished by viewing the gas, electrically illuminated, in a glass bulb. Such tests are made at the Bureau of Standards, the helium for future giant dirigibles being thus sampled.

PARIS FROM AN AIRPLANE

Map-Making from the Sky

THE balloon and airplane are revolutionizing the art of map-making, especially in mountainous regions, and forest or jungle territories. Views of cities from the cloud-land angle have perennial interest, and would seem necromantic had they not become familiar.

Windmills Versus Oil Wells

ANYONE who has visited an oil field will recall that derricks above the oil wells bear a close resemblance to the framework of windmills.

This resemblance is accidental, yet the suggestion of the analogy between the oil well and the windmill is by no means fallacious. Broadly speaking, it may be said that the two have a common object. Both are designed to make energy available for the practical purposes of man's comfort and well-being. Man harnesses energy from natural sources to save himself muscular labor.

The windmill is an ancient device, but until recently it has had limited utility because of practical difficulties in the way of storing the energy that it ensnares. A primitive method was to have the windmill pump water into a tank; but it is obvious that to build a tank large enough or high enough to supply any considerable power involves, under ordinary conditions, an expenditure out of all proportion to the results. The making of a reservoir to hold the water is least feasible in the level countries where the windmill operates most effectively.

So the windmill has waned in popularity, and since the advent of the oil engine the ancient structure has been practically abandoned in most farming communities.

But now we see an illustration of the old law that progress is cyclic. One of the newer uses of the oil engine is to generate electricity to supply electric light and power for farm residences, and this involves the use of a storage battery to bottle up the electricity. Using this apparatus, the farmer became a practical machinist. In particular he learned that all the oil engine does is to turn a wheel, that the energy of molar motion may be transformed by a dynamo, or a generator, into the energy of electricity.

Then why not let a windmill turn the wheel? Oil costs money, whereas the wind is free. Why not use free power?

The experiment was tried, and, of course, it works. The windmill charges the storage batteries just as the oil engine does. So the old problem of storing the energy of the wind is solved.

The Eiffel Tower

THIS spectacular tower, built of iron, in the Champ-de-Mars, Paris, was constructed in 1889, and for many years was the world's highest man-made structure. It is still among the highest, and of unique architectural type.

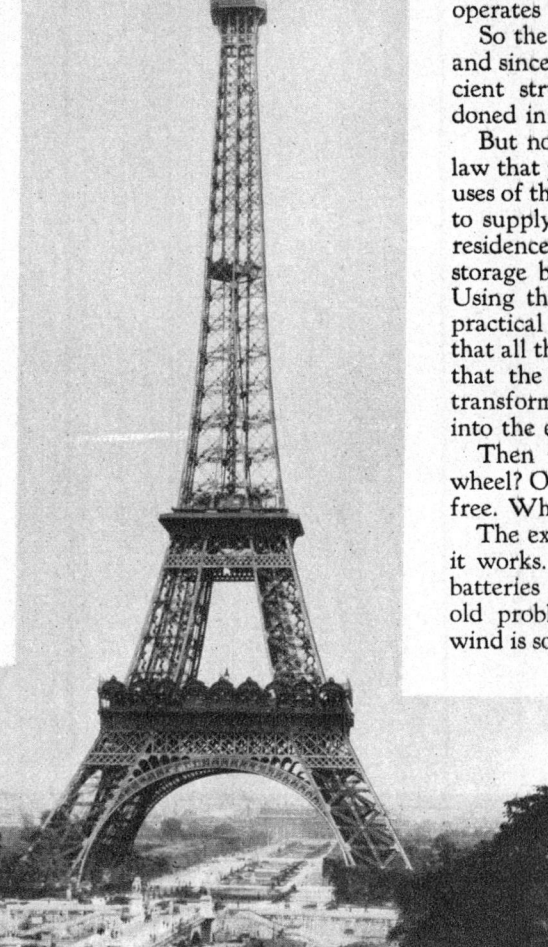

EIFFEL TOWER, PARIS

THE BOOK OF MARVELS

The Tomb of Napoleon

AMONG the most famous of modern monuments; superb in its simplicity. Few sightseers in Paris fail to visit the Hotel des Invalides, to look down into the circular crypt beneath the dome, where the monolithic sarcophagus of red granite stands.

The Cathedral of Notre Dame

THIS cathedral, situated on the Seine, in Paris, is one of the most celebrated of all architectural triumphs of any age. The view that shows it from the air gives an impressive picture of the cathedral itself and its surroundings.

Radio for Bees and Butterflies

IN these days when we are all marveling at the wonders of radio, and feeling pride at the achievement of our race, we are suddenly confronted with the suggestion that man is perhaps the last animal to learn how to interpret radio messages. It is a disconcerting suggestion, but worth considering.

NAPOLEON'S TOMB, PARIS

CATHEDRAL OF NOTRE DAME, PARIS

If you go into the country when the apple trees are in blossom, the hum of bees will come to your ears, and you will see the insects themselves eagerly plying their trade from flower to flower. Their trade, as you know, is to gather nectar to make honey and the wax cells in which to store it.

Naturally you are led to inquire where the hive may be from which the bees have come and to which they will return. And you may be told that no one in the neighborhood keeps bees. There may not be an apiary within several miles.

How, then, did the bees discover the apple tree? And, once they have secured their booty, how do they find their way back home again? It is hard to believe that vision and sense of smell are their only guides.

As another illustration, consider the experiment recorded by Dr. Jacques Loeb, in which a female butterfly was confined in a cigar-box and the box placed indoors, near a window in a country house. Presently a male butterfly of the same species, flying at a distance, changed its course and began fluttering about; then turned at right angles to its former line of flight, and flew directly toward the house and entered at the open window, alighting on the cigar-box that held the captured female.

Apparently there could be no doubt that a message had been received from the captive—some sort of radio message!

Certainly the free butterfly could not see the one in the box. Nor does it seem probable that the sense of smell was the sole guide, if indeed it guided at all.

A more plausible suggestion would seem to be that some aerial vibration, comparable to a radio wave, conveyed the message. The living body, animal or human, is a storehouse of electricity, and exists under certain conditions of what the electrician calls "inductance" and "capacity"; and these conditions, as every radio enthusiast knows, are the ones that determine the sending out and the reception of electromagnetic waves.

The human body has been used as an antennae.

Is it not possible, then, that the butterfly really is a living radio apparatus—that it carries about with it both a sending and a receiving set?

In this connection it is not amiss to recall that the antennae or feelers of insects, and notably those of butterflies and moths, have never been clearly accounted for by the naturalist. The word "antennae" as applied to the radio outfit of human construction was adopted by Marconi because he thought of it as a "feeler" more or less comparable to the antennae of the butterfly. Perhaps he had in mind the close analogy which Dr. Loeb's experiments suggest.

HAULING GREAT LOGS

Light Without Heat

IT has been reported that various scientific workers, both in this country and in Europe, have attained a measure of success in the solution of a problem of enormous practical importance—the production of light without heat.

In the ultra-modern view, it is activities of the electrons, believed to be the ultimate particles of matter, that produce light waves.

These electrons are believed to break away from their atomic moorings whenever the atoms are violently shaken about.

But the only feasible way to produce the right kind of shaking has been through the application of forces that invariably result in heating the substance from which light is to emanate.

This may be done mechanically, as by pounding a piece of iron until it is "red hot"; or chemically, as when we strike a match; or electrically, as when we touch a button and turn on the current to operate the electric light bulb.

But in each case there is a relatively tremendous expenditure of energy in the production of heat, which we perhaps do not wish to produce; whereas only a relatively small amount of the energy manifests itself in the light that we do wish to produce.

Everyone knows that the firefly flashes brilliantly; justifying its colloquial name of lightning bug; while the glowworm gives an amazing imitation of a white-hot coal of fire; and that the insects perform their spectacular feats without being burned. They are producing a "cold" light, thus setting an example for the human inventor.

It is precisely the example of these insects that the human inventors whose relative success is now reported have followed.

The men of science have simply gone to school to the fireflies. They have made chemical examination of the insects' cold-light lantern, and have endeavored, by processes not yet fully revealed, to reproduce in the laboratory a cer-

HARVESTER AND THRESHER

tain organic substance that appears always to be present in the bodies of self-luminous insects of every type.

Why the Draft Horse Is Passing

THE tractor, driven by the gasoline engine, plays many rôles in the present-day industrial world. One Caterpillar tractor here shown is pulling a forty-foot weeder over an Oregon field; another is doing the work of 490 horses, in drawing a multiple harrow; a third hauls a spraying outfit in an irrigated orchard; a fourth pulls a combination harvester and thresher; a fifth hauls logs that no team could handle; and a sixth operates a Canadian snow-plow—where the plowing is good. Such is the power that infinitely small molecules of matter (exploding gas in the cylinders) exert when they act in unison—each molecule merely jostling as hard as it can against all the molecules about it.

The Tide-Predicting Wizard

I SAW a photograph recently showing the wizard-like tide-predicter of the United States Coast and Geodetic Survey, at Washington, in the act of predicting—which in this case is equivalent to determining with unerring accuracy—the tides at Panama. This machine, which is the only one of its kind ever made, can—by proper adjustment—predict the exact time of high and low tide, and the height of the tide, for any given place, for an indefinite time in the future.

WEEDING AN OREGON WHEATFIELD — MODERN STYLE

Since its construction, some years ago, it has been kept busy figuring the tides for all the principal ports in the world a year ahead, doing single-handed the work of sixty human mathematicians. Now it is reported that a recent checking up of actual tides in comparison with predicted tides was made, with the result that the machine was declared to have made its biggest mistake when a particular tide varied from what was foretold by a quarter of an inch.

On the basis of predictions made by human astronomers, the tide-predicting machine has been provided with 37 miniature suns and moons, so adjusted that they can be set in motion by the turning of a crank, and the composite result of their joint action is transmitted to a dial, to be read off and tabulated by a human "operator," who, in effect, acts as stenographer for the brainy machine.

Manipulation is required to adjust the machine for prediction of tides at any particular spot on the coast line of any place in the world. It takes a human mechanician three hours to make this adjustment; and then the machine in seven hours predicts tides for that place for an entire year in advance. Predictions could be made a thousand years ahead as readily as for next year. In practise, they are made two years ahead.

Water and Life

A MAN may fast for thirty or forty days and live to tell the tale, but he cannot go without water for more than a small fraction of that period and survive. No life processes take place except in the presence of moisture. The tissues of the living body are largely composed of water, and the supply must be constantly replenished or all life activities cease.

What applies to human tissues applies to lower organisms as well. The microbes that cause decay can operate only in a moist medium. A perfectly dry tissue—be it meat or fruit or vegetable—does not decay. If moisture is kept from it, it will remain unchanged indefinitely—even for centuries.

It would seem, then, that the ideal way to preserve foodstuffs would be to dry them. Take away the moisture, and no artificial preservative is needed. A perfectly dry beefsteak would be as imperishable as a slab of seasoned wood—say an oak tabletop.

Primitive peoples knew this, though of course they did not know the scientific explanation of the observed fact. The Indians, for example, preserved meat and fruits and vegetables by drying them in the sun or in the smoky air of the wigwam. Familiar present-day foods preserved in a manner scarcely less primitive are dried beef, dried herring, and such vegetable products as dried apples, dried apricots, and prunes and raisins.

Theoretically, nothing should be simpler than to preserve food by removing its moisture. Practically, there may be extreme difficulties in the way of such removal in foods handled on a commercial scale. Somewhat recently, however, these difficulties have been met by the development of drying methods, applicable on a large scale.

SPRAYING

CLEARING SNOW-BLOCKED ROADS

HARROWING

THE BOOK OF MARVELS

Wide World Photograph
TWO-WAY TELEVISION

Television Marvels

THE double transmission of pictures by radio, so that each listener sees the likeness of the other, is a culminating accomplishment of television, as yet only an experimental success, but perhaps to be a commercial method in the not distant future. The transmission of pictures is accomplished with the aid of a "scanning" disc, with a spiral series of holes which "scan" the object to be pictured, permitting reflections that fluctuate with the contour of the face (or light and shadow on a photograph) to modify the current operating through a vacuum-tube of special construction. Television is not a greater, but only a newer, marvel than other radio manifestation.

A Strange Unicycle

WHEN I saw a photograph of the big unicycle that Professor E. J. Christie, of Marion, Iowa, is building my first thought was: "Who ever heard of a one-wheeled vehicle? Why, a unicycle is as much a freak as the traditional unicorn."

And then I reflected that, after all, the wheelbarrow is the original unicycle. But no one looking at Professor Christie's strange vehicle would be likely to think of a wheelbarrow; or of any other preexisting carrier.

The only familiar thing it at all suggests is an overgrown bicycle wheel, with a prolonged axle, from the ends of which wire spokes stretch in double series to the rim, with bird-cage effect.

Within the cage, at the center above the axle, sits the driver with his hands on a steering wheel like that of an automobile.

And now, as we begin to question how the strange craft works, we notice that two other wheels are in evidence. They are perhaps five or six feet in diameter and adjusted to the main axle. Their presence explains the mystery as to how the unicycle is to keep its balance. The two supplementary wheels are to act as gyroscopes.

The DeForest Vacuum Tube

THESE radio tubes of many sizes all operate on the same principle. The principle was the discovery of Lee DeForest, and it is hardly an exaggeration to say that all modern radio development is a by-product of that discovery. The essential involved is the introduction of a third electrode into a vacuum tube, by which the flow of electrons is regulated. The tube that transmits the radio message, the tube that "detects" it, and the tube that magnifies it are but modifications of the same instrument.

Testing a Big Magnet

THE big magnet that I have in mind is the earth itself. That our globe really is a magnet was discovered and demonstrated more than three hundred years ago by William Gilbert, physician in ordinary to Queen Elizabeth, pioneer worker in electricity and outstanding man of genius. He experimented with lodestones shaped into spherical form, and showed that needles or bits of wire laid on such miniature globes come to rest on meridian-lines, like compass needles on earth.

He studied the direction and "dip" of the compass needle itself, and correctly inferred that the magnetic poles of the earth are not located at the geographical poles. The actual magnetic poles—where the compass needle is vertical—are not just where Gilbert theoretically located them, but that is a mere detail. The actual location is a matter of observation, which no one can explain even in our day.

It was Gilbert who first recognized differences between magnetism and electricity. If he were to return to-day, he would find electricity and magnetism working for man in strange coalitions, as in dynamo and telephone. He would hear about marvelous electromagnetic waves used in radio, and would learn that light itself is regarded as an electromag-

Courtesy of the General Electric Co.
THE RADIOTRON FAMILY

TELEVISION APPARATUS

netic phenomenon. He would be told that a unit particle of electricity, called a corpuscle, or electron, has been discovered; and that this smallest of entities is an infinitesimal magnet, just as the earth is a gigantic magnet.

Among other mystifying peculiarities of magnetism is its selective character. The electron, basis of all matter, carries a magnetic field, yet many substances compounded of electrons are non-magnetic. Magnetic force, which may show its power in the handling of tons of metal, has no discoverable influence on the human body. Our bodies feel the pull of gravitation; our senses register the shock of electricity and the contact of heat and light. But magnetism is known to us only at second hand, through its effect on certain metals, notably iron. A "magnetized" body, be it earth or electron, can act across space to pull or push another magnetic body. How this is done, no one knows. Nor does anyone know why the magnetic force, since it acts at all, does not act on all matter impartially, like gravitation. But studies conducted in non-magnetic ships and houses may perhaps give clues to the mystery. The illustration below shows a big man-made magnet at work lifting car-wheels.

NEWS FROM THE SKY

Reporting the News from the Sky

ENGINEERS, reporters, and radio announcers in the cabin of a tri-motored monoplane for observation and radio reporting of the Army Air Corps' raid on New York City, May 22, 1931. Modernity at a climax!

Running Trains by Radio

THE other day out in Pittsburgh a heavily laden freight train was started by radio and ran for some distance without local control. There was an engineer on the locomotive, because the law requires it, but he took no part in the affair until the train was well under way. The man actually in control was the operator at the radio station far away.

One's first thought is that this shows the possibility of transmitting by radio enough power to run a train. But such a thought requires instant revision. Power enough to release a trigger—that is all.

A radio receiving apparatus had been adjusted within the locomotive in such wise that a particular impulse from a radio station would release a lever. This served to set in motion local power in the locomotive or to bring current from a power house along the usual trolley lines.

The radio energy no more propelled the locomotive than the muscle power of an ordinary engineer propels the locomotive when he moves the lever that opens the throttle or turns on a current.

READY TO DIRECT A TRAIN BY RADIO

The Pittsburgh experiment, however interesting, was only an application of the principle developed and illustrated in the "radio car" of Edwin B. Glavin; a little vehicle that runs about and is guided from a distance by its inventor, whose will it seems to obey—and really does obey, provided Mr. Glavin expresses his wishes through the medium of a telegraph key attached to a radio transmitting apparatus.

The power that drives the little automobile forward is located in a storage battery carried within the vehicle itself. But the radio messages establish different circuits at will, and the car responds by turning to right or left, going straight ahead or stopping, as the inventor may direct.

It is fascinating to see the little radio car in action, even though one understands how it is manipulated. The principle of distant control of machinery by radio, demonstrated in Mr. Glavin's little car and on a larger scale in the Pittsburgh freight train, may carry us far in the mechanical world, whether or not the way is found to transmit through the ether enough power to operate the machine as well as control it.

GIANT MAGNET LIFTING CAR-WHEELS

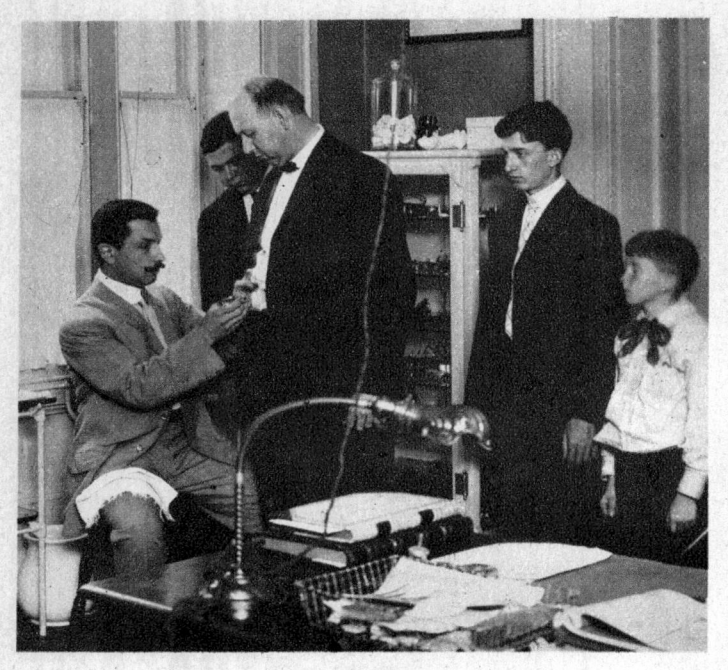

ANTI-RABIES INOCULATION

The Pasteur Institute

REPORT comes from the Pasteur Institute in Paris that a method has been found of developing the germs of tuberculosis through successive cultures until they lose their virulence. There is substantial reason for believing, however, that the germs that have become incapable of menacing the life of an animal are potent to give the animal immunity against tuberculosis.

Should it be possible to make application of this method to the human subject, the importance of the discovery is obvious. But it represents the application of an old method rather than the discovery of a new one. In point of fact, it was by similarly attenuating the virulence of a disease germ that Pasteur himself made the memorable demonstration of the possibility of giving protective immunity as long ago as 1881.

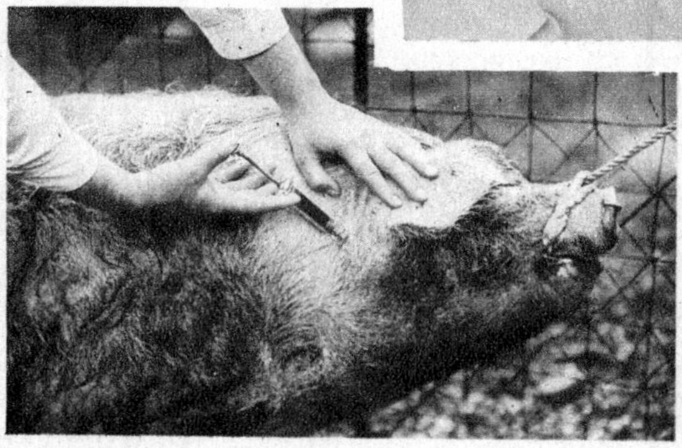

In that year Pasteur demonstrated that he could protect sheep and cattle against anthrax by inoculating them with a vaccine secured by the cultivating of the anthrax bacillus. Twenty-five sheep and goats and five cattle were given a preventive inoculation and subsequently they were inoculated with active virus as were a similar number of animals in an adjoining pen. Two days later all the unprotected animals were dead or dying. The protected ones were well, and so continued.

Pasteur's treatment of hydrophobia followed; and the method of immunization by inoculation with dead germs has become familiar more recently as applied to typhoid fever and some other maladies.

The method has even been extended to tuberculosis, but not to the entire satisfaction of the medical profession. It is to be hoped that the new Pasteur Institute experiments point the way to the development of a completely satisfactory immunizing method that will be another step towards robbing tuberculosis of its terrors. Our pictures show an inoculation against rabies at the Pasteur Institute, and animals used in preparing antitoxic serums.

ANTI-SERUM TO COUNTERACT HOG CHOLERA

Turn About Is Fair Play

NOT many years after my graduation in medicine, I had opportunity to make an experiment which many of my colleagues thought foredoomed to failure.

A partially tamed black-tailed deer in the park at Bloomingdale Asylum (then located where Columbia University now is) ran amuck and attacked an attendant, who defended himself with a rake handle and, striking out vigorously, broke one of the animal's front legs.

My experiment consisted in setting the bone, with application of a plaster of Paris bandage.

This would have been a simple and familiar experience in case of a human patient.

But a deer's leg is so slender and fleshless a member, and the animal itself so far from docile under treatment, that the chance of getting a successful union of the fractured bones seemed more than doubtful.

Nevertheless I thought the attempt worth making. Assisted by my young colleague. Dr. Richard R. Daly (now a noted

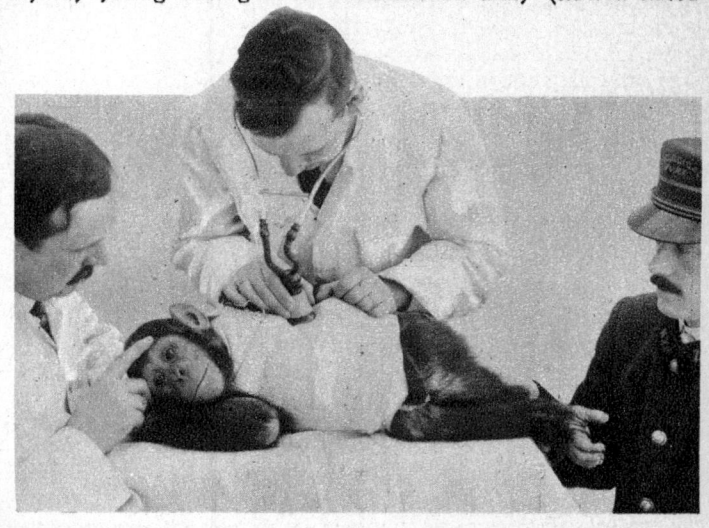

A CHIMPANZEE UNDER TREATMENT

specialist of Atlanta, Georgia), I tied the animal cowboy fashion, and applied the bandage liberally, until the damaged member was held securely in a plaster cast almost as hard as stone.

When, after a suitable interval, the splint was cut away, it was at once apparent that the procedure had been an entire success.

The bones had "knit" perfectly, the leg had not shortened, and only a small nodule, hardly to be noticed by the casual observer, gave evidence of the former injury.

The buck was presently transported to the Bronx Zoological Garden, where it spent the remainder of its life with companions of its species, able to run and jump with the best of them, and in nowise handicapped.

Recollection of this almost forgotten experience came to mind when I saw a photograph showing a group of students at the Pennsylvania Veterinary School in the act of applying bandages to the legs of injured dogs.

The conditions under which they are working are very different from those under which Dr. Daly and I worked forty years ago; yet there is no difference in principle.

We had no glass-topped operating table, and our facilities for practising asepsis were not up to the modern standard; but the result proved that our technique was adequate. The antisepsis, even of that day, was a thoroughly practical method.

I do not mean to imply that there has been no progress in surgical technique in the past third of a century. There has been very notable progress, but it concerns details rather than essentials.

The great revolutionary step had been taken, under guidance of Pasteur and Lister, in the seventh and eighth decades of the nineteenth century. The two young enthusiasts who mended the compound fractured deer's leg in 1889 had a perfectly clear comprehension of the germ theory, and knew just why they were practising antisepsis.

In that day, however, no one had thought of applying the new surgical methods on a comprehensive scale to animals.

Such operating rooms as those of the present Pennsylvania Veterinary School were scarcely dreamed of.

The really notable advance is in practical application of humanitarian principles.

Experiments on animals have taught great lessons in modern therapeutics. It is fitting that afflicted animals, no less than human sufferers, should benefit by the lessons. Turn about is fair play.

Our pictures show a modern operation on a chimpanzee, and the inoculation of a pig against hog cholera.

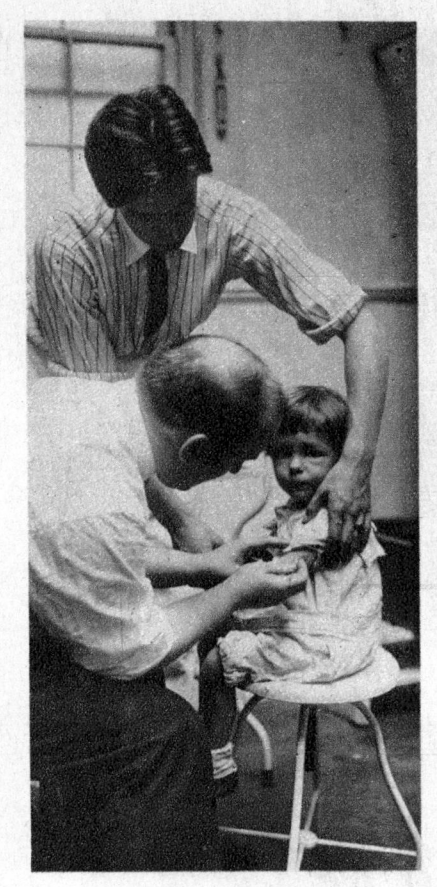

BEING VACCINATED

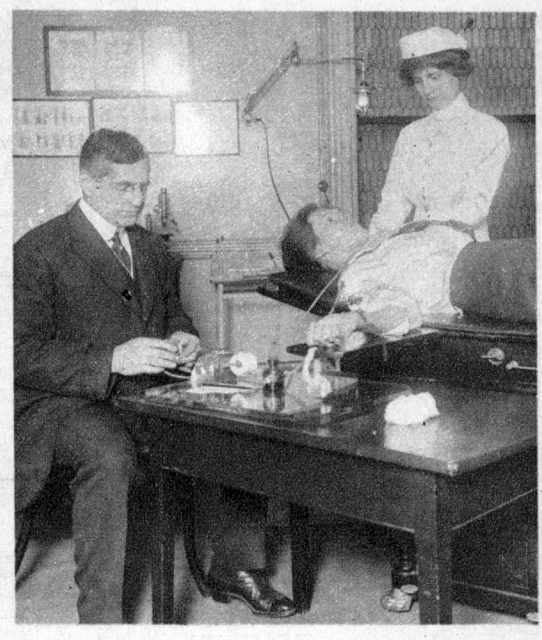

MECHANICAL REGISTRATION OF THE PULSE

Testing the Fire of Life

PHYSICIANS have long been accustomed to speak of the "vital capacity" of an individual as represented by the amount of air that can be breathed out after the deepest possible inhalation.

It is recognized that such a test may have value in determining the state of health of an individual, sometimes, for example, giving premonitions of a tubercular invasion; sometimes being a useful gage of cardiac reserve in cases of heart disease.

The instrument ordinarily used to test vital capacity is known as a spirometer. It may be described as a miniature gas tank. The patient exhales through a tube connected with the cylinder, and the amount of air expelled is registered by a dial.

The instrument has been used not merely by physicians with their patients, but by life insurance companies, in industrial examinations, and among school children.

Among interesting results tabulated are these: (1) Boys show a vital capacity 6 per cent greater than that of girls; (2) the colored race shows a definitely lowered vital capacity; (3) poverty, environment and social status show no influence; (4) malnutrition and underweight for height do not lower the vital capacity.

It follows that a vital capacity below the average or normal standard is indicative of some definite abnormality, and it is held that if the deficiency is 15 per cent, in case of a school child, that child should be singled out for further physical examination in the endeavor to locate the disability.

Somewhat recently it has become possible, through the perfection of apparatus, to extend the respiration tests in such wise as to measure, not the mere quantity of air inhaled, but the amount of oxygen actually consumed by the body in carrying out the vital processes.

If a somewhat spectacular phrasing be permitted, this may be said to measure the fire of life; for, of course, the consumption of oxygen is the essential feature of any burning.

This very searching test of the degree of cellular activity of the body has proved of great diagnostic aid to physicians in conditions of disturbed metabolism (nutrition), particularly when wrong functioning of the thyroid gland is in question.

And now the method is being used to test the fuel consumption associated with various vocational activities—the work of the typist, for example, or of a woman operating a sewing machine, or of a man driving a bicycle.

TESTING BLOOD PRESSURE

Testing Heart Action

THE action of the heart is tested in many ways by the modern specialist. The pictures show one type of blood-pressure testing (by noting the pressure of a mercury-column that just shuts off the arterial circulation), and a mechanically registering pulse-tester, the records of which are quite meaningless except to the special student of heart-action.

A GREAT MODERN REFLECTING TELESCOPE

Canada's Largest Telescope

THIS is the great reflector of the Dominion Observatory, the finest Canadian instrument, and one of the finest telescopes in the world. It is so installed that the supporting pivotal column is parallel to the earth's axis; therefore the telescope tube, as the axis revolves, follows the movements of the star-field on which it is focused. Every great modern telescope is thus mounted at a particular angle determined by the latitude of the place where it operates. The movement of the great tube is of course effected by mechanical power, operated by clockwork. But the principle was utilized by ancient star-gazers with their "quadrants" long before telescopes were invented.

Signals from Mars

IT is commonly assumed that the Martian, if he exists at all, has a much older civilization than our own. The basis for this assumption is the nebular hypothesis, according to which the various planets were thrown off in succession from the mass of world-stuff which contracted as it cooled, with the sun at its center. On this thesis the outer planets would obviously be older and Mars would presumably have been far ahead of us in developing a living population.

We might fairly expect our elder planetary brother to take the initiative in sending signals to the earth. Radio, which is new with us, may be an old, old story with the Martians. Quite possibly they have been patiently waiting thousands of years for us to become intelligent enough to answer their signals. More than likely they persecuted their Galileo for teaching that Mars is not the center of the universe while our ancestors were still in the tree-tops, and their last William J. Bryan, fatuously denying the simple truths of evolution, may have passed from the scene long before we were intelligent enough to give any thought at all to our origin.

If the Martian exists, and if he has a radio system that can reach the earth, he should have no difficulty in revealing himself to us. Nothing more would be necessary than to send a series of signals at fixed intervals. If, for example, he were to make two signals, then after an interval two more, and after a double interval, four signals, we should know that he was proving that he could add two and two.

Similarly it has been suggested that the Martians might make signs by digging long canals, such as those that some astronomers think they have observed. Nature, it is noted, favors curves rather than straight lines. If you were to find four or five trees growing by themselves in a straight line, you would know that they had been planted by an intelligent being. There are no straight rivers nor perfectly straight coast lines in Nature's plan. So if it could be shown that there are long straight canals on Mars, that would be accepted as evidence of the presence of intelligent beings there.

The Striped Jacket of Jupiter

THE planet Jupiter, largest member of the sun's family, has a curiously striped appearance, when photographed with the aid of a powerful telescope. The rings shown in the photograph by Dr. E. C. Slipher, of Lowell Observatory, are in nowise similar to the rings of Saturn. They are due to conditions on the planet itself or in its atmosphere. But precisely what these conditions are is conjectural.

Measuring the Universe

AMONG the very few women to gain distinction as original discoverers in astronomy was Miss Leavitt, long connected with the Harvard University Observatory. Working with the apparatus shown at her right, Miss Leavitt studied the varying brightness of certain stars found scattered through globular clusters. These so-called Cepheid Variables appear to pulsate rhythmically, growing brighter and then diminishing with regularity, but with varying intervals. Miss Leavitt discovered that all stars having pulsation-periods of less than one day are faint stars; those of longer period are brighter. This notable observation led Professor Hertzsprung, of Leyden, and Professor Harlow Shapley, now of Harvard, to develop a method of testing the distance of stars by their "period luminosity," with the result that astronomers now talk about stars a million light-years distant quite casually.

TYCHO BRAHE'S QUADRANT

A Star Cluster

ROUND star clusters are a type apart. They are far less numerous than nebulae. Their main distribution in restricted segments of the firmament adds to the mystery of their origin and significance. They contain many variable stars, of a peculiar

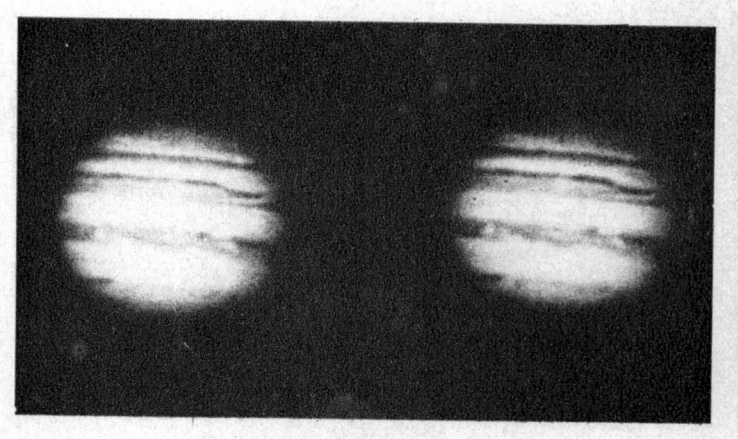

JUPITER'S STRIPED JACKET

type, which change their brightness with regularity, and which have aided the astronomers in measuring star-distances. The clue is found in a not very clearly explained relationship between period of variation in brightness and actual brightness of the different variables.

Build Your Own Telescope

IT is claimed by Mr. C. E. Barnes, a member of the American Astronomical Society, that practically anyone who wishes to become an observing astronomer may do so. You have but to build your own reflecting telescope and set to work star-gazing.

Mr. Barnes knows whereof he speaks, for he is the possessor of a homemade telescope with which he can see "the marvels of the moon in first quarter, the belts and moons of Jupiter, the crescent of Venus, the rings of Saturn, the snowcaps of Mars, and such stellar wonders as clusters, nebulae, and multiples." Quite a telescope, you will agree. And it was acquired by "the exercise of ordinary skill and ingenuity, a resolve to get up an hour earlier each morning for a few weeks, and—a total expenditure of twenty-six dollars and thirty cents."

The essentials are—a piece of plate glass ten inches across and at least an inch and a half thick, with ground edges; another piece of plate glass not quite so large or so thick, to serve as grinding tool; half a pound each of five or six grades of carborundum, from "40" to "200," and a pound of the finest emery powder for grinding and finishing; some ordinary black pitch and some grafting wax for polishing; and a reasonable stock of patience and perseverance.

The large piece of plate glass is to be ground by hand, with the aid of the abrasives, until its surface is concave, a little deeper at the center, to make a paraboloid curved so that rays of light falling on it when it is placed at the bottom of the telescope tube will be sent back to a focus at a predetermined point near the top of the tube, where a plane mirror reflects them out through an eyepiece. The tube of the telescope must, of course, be mounted so that it can be rotated to point at any heavenly body that the observer may wish to see.

Mr. Barnes speaks of a ten-inch mirror, and that is sufficient to satisfy most amateur ambitions. Still it should not be forgotten that the man who is remembered as perhaps the greatest observing astronomer that ever lived, Sir William Herschel, constructed with his own hands (with the aid of his sister) the five-foot mirror with which he made the amazing observations that marked a new epoch in modern astronomy. The recollection of that success should fortify the most vaulting ambition.

HERCULES STAR CLUSTER

HERSCHEL AND ONE OF HIS HAND-MADE TELESCOPES

MISS LEAVITT AT HARVARD OBSERVATORY

The Brain-Making Thyroid

IT is a well-established belief among physicians that the condition known as cretinism is due primarily to a deficiency of the secretion of the thyroid gland. The cretin is dwarfed in mind and body. Administration of thyroid extract sometimes results in very marked amelioration of the defective conditions.

Peculiar interest attaches to the series of experiments conducted by Dr. Frederick S. Hammett, of the Wistar Institute of Anatomy and Biology, in Philadelphia, of which the subjects have been specialized races of white rats. Entire litters of these animals have been subjected to removal of the thyroid apparatus, including the tiny glands called parathyroids, and comparison made between the subsequent development of such animals and their normal litter-brethren; all the animals being of course, kept on the same diet and under precisely similar hygienic conditions in general.

That the thyroidless rats should suffer retarded physical development was to be expected; and when the final examination was made fifty days after the operation, the scales amply confirmed the expectation. But, it seemed desirable in particular to test the comparative development of the brain and spinal cord.

It appears that the brain of the thyroidless rats suffered retarded development quite out of proportion to the body in general, and even greatly in excess of the spinal cord. Moreover, the brains of the females were much more markedly affected than those of the males. Indeed, it would appear that the brains of females, lacking the thyroid-stimulus, practically ceased to develop; specifically, they showed three per cent of the development of brains of normal animals, as against the twenty-one per cent development of the brains of the thyroidless males.

The Grand Canyon of the Colorado

CONCEDED by every observer to be one of the most extraordinary natural spectacles in the world, this canyon has altogether exceptional scientific interest as well. The horizontal strata, elevated thousands of feet from their original sea-bed level, have been cut through by the river (the water remaining at about the same level as the land rose) somewhat as a saw cuts through a log of wood—to use an illustration credited to Major Powell, who first explored the Canyon. The strata in the walls reveal the geological history of the world through successive ages incomparably, and the Canyon as a whole gives matchless object lessons in the mechanics of transformation by erosion.

GRAND VIEW TRAIL, GRAND CANYON OF THE COLORADO

The great and novel merit of Mr. Johnson's radio apparatus is that it is readily portable, requiring neither aerial nor "ground," and being operated solely by small dry-cell batteries, like those of an ordinary call-bell. The transmitting radiophone is adjusted on a portable tripod. The receiver is in effect a hoop, to be held in the hand.

Half Dome from Glacier Point

THIS mountain peak, rising five thousand feet from the Yosemite Valley, is composed of metamorphic or granitic rock that has been upheaved from the original ocean-bed of its

Courtesy of the National Park Service
Photograph by H. T. Cowling
HERMIT TRAIL, GRAND CANYON NATIONAL PARK

Radio to Safeguard Miners

IT is with peculiar satisfaction that one learns of the invention of a new device that gives promise of lessening the dangers of underground and undersea work, through making constant communication with the normal world possible.

The device in question is, as might be anticipated, a type of radio apparatus. It is capable, we are told, of sending the voice through stone walls or coal beds two hundred feet in thickness.

When miners are entombed by the caving in of a shaft—a catastrophe seemingly unavoidable now and then—it is always difficult, and sometimes impossible, to communicate with them. Indistinct tappings convey at best very vague information, and the rescue parties work at a constant disadvantage.

It is hoped that the new radio device, invented by Bernays Johnson, will make such rescue work in future very much more effective. The imprisoned men will be able to talk with their would-be rescuers, insuring a measure of cooperation not otherwise to be hoped for.

HALF DOME FROM GLACIER POINT, YOSEMITE VALLEY

THE BOOK OF MARVELS

origin to the present almost perpendicular position. According to the newest theory, such crumpling up of strata to form mountains, along the western coast of our continent, was caused by the westward drift of the continent itself, opposed by the viscidity of the molten matter in which the continent then floated. The upheaved strata have of course been enormously eroded since their elevation, to give the conical form now observed.

How Glaciers Work

GLACIERS are in effect rivers of ice. They move slowly, but they persistently move. And the weight of the ice-mass is so great that its eroding and transporting power is enormous.

A GLACIER ON MOUNT RAINIER

A MAN-MADE LAKE

The phenomena of glaciers in the Alps led to the conception of general glaciation over wide territories, which eventuated in the glacial theory of Agassiz, now generally accepted as the explanation of a notable series of geological manifestations.

An Artificial Lake Near San Diego

A SUPERB dam of arched masonry blocks the outlet of an ancient lake bed, and produces a reservoir that stores water for the ultimate irrigation of thousands of acres of citrus groves and truck gardens in southern California. The spectacular transformation from desert to garden by such reclamation schemes gives object lessons that never cease to cause astonishment.

A Giant Geyser

THIS is the "Old Faithful" geyser, of the Yellowstone National Park. Geysers send forth spouts of water intermittently, actuated by steam which accumulates in the depths of the earth. They afford a tangible demonstration of the fact of interior heat of the earth's crust. Hitherto no practical

"OLD FAITHFUL" GEYSER, YELLOWSTONE PARK

use has been made of the energy thus liberated. But the geyser points the way to future tapping of the earth's interior heat for commercial purposes. It has been suggested that the value of an invention that would permit such tapping of earth-heat on a large scale would be measured in billions of dollars. "Old Faithful" throws a spout of 150 feet every 63 minutes.

Oil for Troubled Waters

IF you have been at sea in a storm or have stood by the shore when the breaking waves dashed high, you have gained an awesome impression of stupendous and seemingly irresistible powers in remorseless operation. It is hard to conceive that any man-made apparatus could cope with such colossal engines of destruction as the ocean waves.

Yet it is known that these waves are, in reality, only surface phenomena. They represent the oscillation of what, by comparison, is only a thin film of water. The vast bulk of water beneath them, which would indeed be irresistible, does not contribute to their power, and, although their capacity for destructive action is certainly not to be taken lightly, they are by no means untamable. An expedient simple as the shearing of the locks of a traditional Samson may rob them of a large measure of their power.

Everyone knows what this expedient is, for the phrase about pouring oil on troubled waters has a secure place among what might be termed household metaphors; and the metaphor is founded on literal fact. A small quantity of oil dribbled onto the surface of the sea spreads rapidly in every direction, and strangely operates to smooth out the angry waves and make them harmless. Such an effect is much too unplausible to have been predicted, but the phenomenon appears to have been observed in remote times, and modern tests have abundantly re-demonstrated its validity.

A HAPPY CHIMPANZEE. NOT SUZETTE BUT ONE OF HER COUSINS

The Strength of Suzette

SHE was formerly a professional bicycle rider and roller skater, traveling with a circus, but she developed a treacherous temper that made her unreliable, and her manager retired her. She took up domestic life with a chap named Boma, and two children have been born to them, both of which, however, died in infancy.

Our present concern, however, is not with Suzette's domestic affairs, but with the record of her athletic prowess as manifested in some recent private exhibitions. The question at issue concerned the relative strength of members of the race of Chimpanzees, to which Suzette belongs, and athletes of our own race.

The tests were carried out at the New York Zoological Park by John E. Bauman. The results were such as to make the human athlete feel anything but "chesty."

For little Suzette, who is a legitimate lightweight, stripping 135 pounds, gave a tug at the dynamometer rope that registered 1,260 pounds on the dial of the recording device.

An average college student of her weight, under similar conditions, can register about 332 pounds, and one student in a hundred can pull 500 pounds. A champion athlete may record about half the strength of little Sister Sue.

It is obvious that the young woman would be a very disagreeable antagonist in a hair-pulling contest; but it would probably be unwise for her to "start anything" in that line in her own family, for her paramour, Boma, has muscles of his own that should prove quite adequate for defense.

He has scorned to enter into a contest that would demonstrate his full strength; but on one occasion he did give a playful one-handed pull at the rope and registered 847 pounds. Another one-hand pull of 640 pounds seemed to cost him no effort whatever.

Boma is a middle-weight, tipping the beam at about 165 pounds. The investigator who saw him register with one hand, a pull beyond the strength of a human athlete using every muscle, was led to wonder what might be the limits of power of a gorilla weighing 450 pounds.

An Extraordinary Bird City

A COLONY of flamingoes nesting, as reproduced in the American Museum of Natural History, New York.

JOHN DANIEL, FAMOUS GORILLA

FLAMINGO COLONY

Sword Bearers of the Sea

OF the many strange creatures in the sea, the sawfish is not the least strange. Offhand, one does not realize at a glance how its curious weapon can give service to its possessor that will outbalance the disadvantages of lugging about such an encumbrance. But the fact that the sawfishes have lived and thrived and multiplied for ages shows that the strange weapon has genuine utility.

Something of the uses to which the sawfish puts his weapon may be inferred from observation of the swordfish, a creature of very different type in the eye of the zoologist, but provided with a swordlike weapon in all respects similar to that of the other except that it lacks teeth along the edges.

WHITE WHALE, THE RACE-HORSE OF THE DEEP

MODERN WHALING BOAT

A BIG CATCH

The swordfish, as I am assured by fishermen who have had abundant opportunities to observe it, makes good use of its weapon in capturing its prey. It will drive into a school of mackerel and thrust out with its sword, lashing this way and that, to the destruction of any number of mackerel, the bodies of which it subsequently picks up at its leisure.

Moreover, the sword may be an effective weapon of defense as well. When a fisherman harpoons the swordfish, and attempts to haul it to the surface, the creature will on occasion turn on its captor and make a dash at his boat. The fisherman then clambers quickly on the seat of his dory, knowing that the weapon of the fish will run clear through the bottom of the boat.

It appears, too, that this natural sword is an excellent dueling weapon. Sometimes a shark attacks a swordfish, making a dash in the endeavor to bite off the tail (or "flukes" in fisherman's parlance), which would render the swordfish helpless. When this attack fails, the swordfish is likely to turn quickly on its assailant, and pierce the shark's body through and through with that deadly weapon.

From Whale to Dynamo!

IN the days of our grandparents many hundreds of vessels sailed from New England ports in quest of whales. It is recorded that from New Bedford alone more than five hundred whaling vessels weighed anchor, with aggregate crews of twenty thousand men.

The chief products brought back by the whalers were whalebone and sperm oil. At that time no substitute for the elastic "bone" had been found; and sperm oil, the artificial light-producer de luxe, held a high place among the "modern" products conceded to be indispensable.

There was free prophecy, on the part of the wiseacres, that a permanent whale shortage would plunge the world in darkness, to the serious crippling of civilization itself.

But the whaling industry was profitable, and it was prosecuted with such assiduity that presently the supply diminished to the vanishing point.

Indeed, it is rather a surprize to learn that there are still whalers sailing from New England ports. Yet such is the fact; and we are told also of whaling stations of the Far North and Far South which do a flourishing business.

South Georgia Island, for example, is said to have six whaling stations employing a thousand men and producing about 240,000 barrels of whale oil annually.

Several species of whale furnish the oil, but the sperm whale is the most highly prized producer.

A small part of the oil is used in the making of a superior brand of candles; but the major part of it is used for the purposes of machine lubrication.

The mineral oil well, the gas plant, and the electric-light generating dynamo have put the whale quite out of the running as a producer of artificial daylight.

Doubtless the dynamo should be largely credited with saving the whales from extermination. At any rate it is gratifying to know that the great creatures still exist in considerable numbers.

Though so similar in general appearance, they are curiously diversified in habit, ranging from the mild-mannered whale-bone producer, which strains animalcules and jelly-fishes out of the water for food, and the sperm whale, which feeds largely on squids, to the small but ferocious "killer," which attacks the behemoths of its own race, biting out their tongues (so the whalers declare), and ultimately feasting on the carcasses of its victims.

96　　　　　　　　　　THE BOOK OF MARVELS

PROTECTIVE COLORING OF A RATTLESNAKE

Camouflage

EVERYONE who has been much in the open is familiar with examples of so-called "protective coloration." Prairie birds have the color of grass and earth; the little brown creeper, running along the trunk of a tree, looks like a piece of bark; the "tree-toad" takes the color of whatever surface he perches on; and various insects, including some of the large moths, are permanently colored in imitation of the different surfaces on which they habitually rest.

But of course the camouflaging is not limited to color-effect. So familiar an insect as the "walking-stick" has the shape and appearance of a twig. Often you must touch it and make it move to determine that it is a

RESEMBLING A KNOT HOLE

THE WALKING LEAF

living thing. Even more spectacular resemblances of this type are illustrated by such a tropical insect as the walking leaf and various leaflike butterflies which, when perching, have every appearance of being permanently attached to the twig.

A curious feature of the insect disguise, as applied to some of the moths and butterflies, is that the protective coloration extends only to one surface of the wings, or to one pair of wings. A butterfly, for example, may be extremely conspicuous, even brilliantly colored, on the upper surface of its wings, so that it has a high degree of visibility when in flight; and yet may disappear altogether, becoming a leaf to all appearances in both shape and color, when it folds the wings above its back and attaches itself to a twig.

BUTTERFLY RESEMBLING LEAF

A Plant That Eats Flies

ALL plants that contain the green coloring matter called chlorophyl have the power (possessed by them alone) of extracting carbon from the air, and synthesizing the basic sugars that are the foundation of what becomes protoplasm, the life-substance, when further combined with nitrogen. Thus there could be no animal life except as plant life prepares the way for it, and perpetually sustains it. It is no more than a fair turn-about, then, that here and there a plant should develop the capacity to imbibe animal matter, as the pitcher plant here shown is able to do. The habit of catching insects and ingesting their substance is so unusual, however, that it seems quite marvelous. In the aggregate, the number of carnivorous plants is large; but in the relative scale—contrasted with the myriads of plants that ingest only inorganic matter—they are almost negligible. And even these exceptional plants depend only in minor degree on such food; whereas every animal, of whatever degree, is exclusively dependent on plants, in the last analysis, for sustenance.

A PLANT THAT EATS FLIES

Photograph by Underwood and Underwood

HATCHING AN ALLIGATOR

Hatching an Alligator

REPTILES, like birds (which, historically speaking, are only modified reptiles), are produced from eggs. Like birds, the young reptiles are provided with a horny growth at the tip of their upper jaw, which enables them to penetrate the shell, and liberate themselves. The alligators represent one of the five Orders of Reptiles that survived the Mesozoic Era, or Age of Reptiles. All representatives of fourteen other Orders became extinct.

MOTH RESEMBLING BARK

Self-Defense for Fishes and Nations

AT the New York Aquarium you may see a little six-inch fish called the "puffer," which can swell up to "the size of your hat."

A little puffer fish swelled up to absurd proportions is in itself a grotesque object. But when we know that the ludicrous transformation is effected in order to save the creature's life by keeping some larger fish from swallowing it, we reflect that here is a particular instance of the general law of self-preservation that applies to all living creatures, including man, and even to the aggregations of men that we call nations.

Some creatures, in order to defend themselves, are given long legs or strong wings or other organs of locomotion to enable them to flee swiftly. Others are given teeth and claws to enable them to fight. Many marine creatures, after the manner of the oyster, are encased in protective shells. Many creatures of both sea and land are given protective coloration, so that they are relatively invisible.

From each and all, man has taken lessons. He has invented mechanisms for fleeing and for fighting, and has learned to practise elaborate methods of camouflage on both sea and land. And by no means has he neglected the peculiar method of the puffer fish, which, as applied to human affairs, may be characterized by the colloquial term "bluffing."

Probably that thought was at the back of M. Clemenceau's head as he watched the maneuvering of the puffer fish, and said, "Just like a nation."

JOHN FITCH'S STEAMBOAT

MODEL OF STERN-WHEEL STEAMER, *CHARLOTTE DUNDAS*

MODEL OF STEVENS'S TWIN-SCREW STEAMBOAT

The First American Steamboat

IT seems fairly certain that the first American steamboat was made by John Fitch, of Philadelphia. Whether this boat antedated the Scottish steamboat *Charlotte Dundas* is not so certain. The New York Historical Society dates Fitch's boat "about 1776." Other records suggest the first launching as of ten years later—which would give the Scottish boat precedence. In any event, Fitch's boat was probably originated quite independently. The model shows it with both screw propeller and paddle-wheel, and with the most primitive type of steam engine imaginable. It may be recalled that Watt's first patent on his perfected steam engine was taken out in 1769. But the steam pump of Newcomen, with which Watt first experimented, was patented more than a half century earlier, and may well have been known to Fitch. Regardless of its antecedents, the steamboat of Fitch was a generation ahead of its time, and there was no sequel to its exhibition. The suggestion that a pumping machine might take the place of good substantial oars operated by strong arms must have seemed grotesque to all beholders. Yet James Watt in Scotland was even then making two improvements destined to bring the engine into our present-day life. One was the double use of steam —at the two ends of the cylinder—and the other was a new device for utilizing its expansive force

The First Man-Sized Steamboat

NOT Fulton's *Clermont*, as is often supposed, but a Scottish boat named the *Charlotte Dundas,* which was a double-hulled pleasure boat that was propelled at a speed of five miles an hour on the Clyde in 1788. A reconstruction of the marine engine that drove its paddle-wheels is here shown, with models of the wheels. Here we have the original of Fulton's more famous boat; and the maker of this engine, William Symington, is seldom named in casual histories of great inventions. It was rumored that Fulton visited Scotland, and actually rode on the *Charlotte Dundas* many years before his Hudson-River triumph of 1807. It is not alone in our day that publicity counts in the making of reputations.

The First Twin-Screw Propeller

FULTON'S steamboat was propelled by paddle-wheels. But a boat made by Stevens several years before the *Clermont* steamed up the Hudson used the screw-propeller principle. More than that, it set the example of the double propeller, which was not generally followed for several decades after screw-propelled steamboats came into vogue. The photograph shows the original engine of the inventor, made about the year 1800. The model of the boat is a restoration, in the Smithsonian Institution, Washington. Nothing whatever appears to have come, directly at any rate, of the prevision of the man-before-his-time who believed—and demonstrated—that boats could be propelled by a steam engine causing propellers to revolve. Yet this is precisely the manner of propulsion of every modern ocean-going steamship—to say nothing of the airplane and the Zeppelin.

Monuments That Live and Grow

ALL civilization is founded on a few great inventions, and the major part of these are of nameless origin. Nobody knows who first conceived the value of artificial fire, or who first smelted metals, or first made pottery, or conceived the idea of depicting thoughts in the form of words. No one knows who first used a lever, or first made a boat, or contrived the marvelous invention called a wheel.

No one knows who first domesticated animals, or who first practised the art of agriculture. We do not know the names of the ancient Burbanks who gave us cultivated varieties of wheat, oats and rye and of most types of orchard fruits. If the names of these men of genius were ever matters of historical record, the records have been obliterated.

Exception must be made, however, of a few varieties of fruits that have been developed within the past century or two, with which the names of their developers have been associated in common usage. Three such examples, familiar to every orchardist, are the Baldwin apple and the Seckel and Bartlett pears. The trees on which these fruits grow constitute perpetual monuments to their originators—monuments that grow and develop, and spread across the zones, perennially benefiting mankind physically just as works of art benefit us mentally and spiritually.

STEAMSHIP *BREMEN*

The Newest Type of Ocean Grayhound

THE modern steamship, in itself marvelous, seems doubly so when we contrast with it the steamships of even a generation ago—to say nothing of the primitive types of the early nineteenth century. This is the German liner, named the *Bremen*.

Wearers of Shells

IT must be inconvenient to carry one's house about with one, but the creatures that do it act from necessity. Without their shell-houses, they would soon fall victim to their enemies. They have developed shells in place of weapons of defense such as the skunk and the porcupine have, for example; or speedy organs of locomotion, like those of rabbits and fishes. Obviously, a tortoise without its shell would not last long in a predatory world. Even shorter would be the life of shell-less oysters and a host of other sea-bed dwellers. The oyster's shell is hinged, and the two parts are held together by strong muscles—but even so, the starfish is able to get the shell open, and devour its occupant. The creatures called cephalopods, of which the "pearly" nautilus is a well-known example, early learned to build spiral shells, which clearly are harder to get into (for the enemy) than straight shells would be. Geological records tell of times when conditions of life became peculiarly hard for some of the shell-bearers, and the fossils show shells curiously contorted and double-twisted. Presumably there were enemies that found their way into the depths of the shells; for these contorted creatures presently became extinct. The so-called Ammonites, shells coiled like rams' horns, are notable examples. The picture shows the most familiar modern shell-bearer, the tortoise.

A TORTOISE, MOST FAMILIAR OF LARGE SHELL-BEARERS

Concrete Ships

TOWARD the close of the World War word came from the Pacific Coast of the launching of the largest concrete ship hitherto constructed—a vessel 320 feet long and having 7,900 gross tonnage. No movable monolith of similar dimensions ever existed before anywhere in the world

As a matter of course, the concrete used in making such a ship is reinforced with rods of steel. But the amount of steel required has been reduced to a minimum, the individual pieces being welded together to prevent overlapping; and if the original plans have been carried out the total reinforcement weighs less than the bolts needed in a wooden ship of equal dimensions.

Moreover, the reinforced concrete hull as a whole will weigh less than that of a wooden ship—a really surprizing fact, explained by the relative thinness of the stone shell. The stone ship appears to have been only a war-time makeshift. But a floating monolith is an interesting paradox.

The First Commercial Steamboat (Restored)

THE famous steamboat of Fulton was not in reality the first boat to be propelled by steam. It is even alleged that Fulton had himself seen the experimental boat that operated on a river in Scotland upward of twenty years before the *Clermont* made its memorable trip up the Hudson. But to Fulton belongs the unquestioned honor of making the steamboat a commercial craft. In its day, the first commercial steamboat was regarded as one of the wonders of the world. People in general were as skeptical of the possibility of operating a boat by steam at the beginning of the nineteenth century, as they were of making a heavier-than-air machine fly at the beginning of the twentieth century.

Nor was the full value of steam as a propellant realized, even by forward-looking men, for a long time after Fulton's memorable demonstration. The *Clermont* steamed up the Hudson in 1807, and continued in operation for many years. But even the inventor himself appears not to have thought of steam craft as other than river boats. About a third of a century passed before the first steamboat crossed the Atlantic.

FULTON'S *CLERMONT*

THE BOOK OF MARVELS

FOSSIL SKELETONS OF GIANT SLOTHS

A Paradoxical Animal

THE sloth spends most of its time upside down—hanging from the branches of trees. Sometimes it takes on the color of leaves, from algae that grow on its hair. Outwardly, it thus becomes part vegetable, which seems not inappropriate. The other picture shows fossil skeletons of an ancestor of the sloth, which grew to great size, and lived on the ground, but walked awkwardly, on the sides of its feet, in reminiscence of its former arboreal habit. Gigantic ground sloths lived in California at a geologically recent period.

Artificial Lightning

THIS "spark-over" between electrodes nine feet apart, with current at a million volts, may justly be spoken of as "artificial lightning." The demonstration was made at the high-voltage engineering laboratory of the General Electric Company, at Pittsfield, Mass. It is said that current transmission at a million volts was never before accomplished.

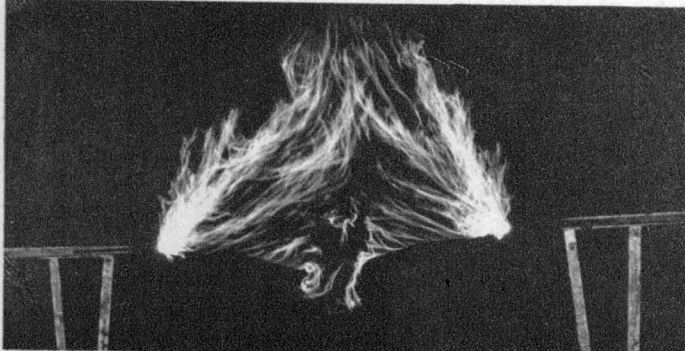

Courtesy of the General Electric Co.
ARTIFICIAL LIGHTNING

Chemistry Through the Microscope

IN the popular mind, chemistry is associated with test-tubes and crucibles. But the modern chemist has other weapons. Chemistry has many branches, and a specialist in one line may use an equipment that would not answer at all for another type of investigation. Thus chemical reactions ordinarily take place between agents in solution, as in many simple test-tube experiments; but, on the other hand, an entire series of investigations may concern elements that are permanently gaseous. Certain components of the atmosphere were undiscovered until recent times—had been overlooked in thousands of air analyses—because they will not combine with anything and must be tested with an instrument borrowed from the physical laboratory, a so-called spectroscope that reveals certain tell-tale lines in the visible spectrum. One of these atmospheric gases is helium, which was discovered in the sun long before its presence on our globe was suspected.

The spectroscope enables the chemist to reach out to the stars and record the composition of luminous bodies so distant that the light which bears the message has reached us only after journeying for years, or even centuries, at a speed of 186,000 miles per second.

Again, there are lines of chemical investigation that deal with matter neither as gas nor as liquid, but in solid form; in particular with crystals, the most condensed of solids. In a laboratory of the Public Health Service at Washington, you might find a worker like Dr. E. T. Wherry, of the Bureau of Chemis-

MODERN SLOTH IN NORMAL ATTITUDE

try, peering hour after hour through a so-called petrographic microscope, intently observing the precise appearance of one field of crystals after another, and drawing inferences from what he sees as to the purity or impurity of foodstuffs.

Such an examination may reveal at a glance the presence of a chemical that could otherwise be detected only by an elaborate examination—of test-tube and crucible type—requiring hours or days. For a very large number of substances assume characteristic forms on crystallizing, and can thus be at once detected under the magnifying lens. So the microscope, like the spectroscope, though dealing with physical properties of matter, may become an indispensable adjunct of the chemical laboratory.

Diamond Cut Diamond

IF you were shown two primitive stone arrow-heads, one of chipped flint, the other smoothly polished, and were asked to indicate the one that you could more readily duplicate, you would almost surely select the smooth one. Smoothing things by friction is to you a familiar process—as in sharpening a knife or pointing a lead pencil. But unless you chance to be a stonecutter, you have had little experience that would suggest the manner of procedure to be adopted in chipping a piece of flint into the shape of a symmetrical arrow-head.

Yet our primitive ancestors found out how to make implements of chipped stone, and were able to fashion these into beautiful symmetrical forms, ages before they conceived the possibility of making implements of any kind by the frictional or

CANDLEMAKER

DIAMOND CUTTING

polishing method. In studying the records of prehistoric man, the "rough stone" age is found to antedate the "smooth stone" age. The race that learned to polish stone had taken a long step forward.

The polishing of diamonds into "brilliants" with symmetrical facets is a modern art, originating seemingly with Ludwig van Berquen, who flourished at Bruges about the year 1460. His method, which is still followed with little modification, involves cleaving the rough stone with a knife; "bruting" it into symmetrical form by rubbing it against another diamond; and polishing the many facets by holding the stone, partly embedded in a soft metal matrix, against a fast-revolving wheel coated with diamond dust.

The wheel, horizontally arranged, is called a "skeif." Four mechanical arms hold as many diamonds against the revolving surface, and a single operator manipulates these arms to modify the pressure. When a facet is polished sufficiently the diamond is removed from the metal matrix and re-embedded at a different angle.

A Mechanical Candlemaker

EVEN in this day of electricity, the old-fashioned candle is by no means obsolete. This machine makes 96 candles at a single cast. The wicks are supplied from bobbins. Water jackets surround the molds, minimizing the time between casts.

Ninety-Two Blades

A MARVELOUS knife, surely—an instrument with not far from a hundred blades. One marvels most of all, perhaps, that the ingenious maker of the instrument did not round out the number of its blades to the even hundred. Of course no new principle is involved in the construction of the rather grotesque implement. It is merely a freak, interesting as illustrating what painstaking human effort may accomplish. One hopes that the maker of the knife got a lot of pleasure out of his task and, no doubt, it also justifies its existence as an advertising medium for the manufacturer.

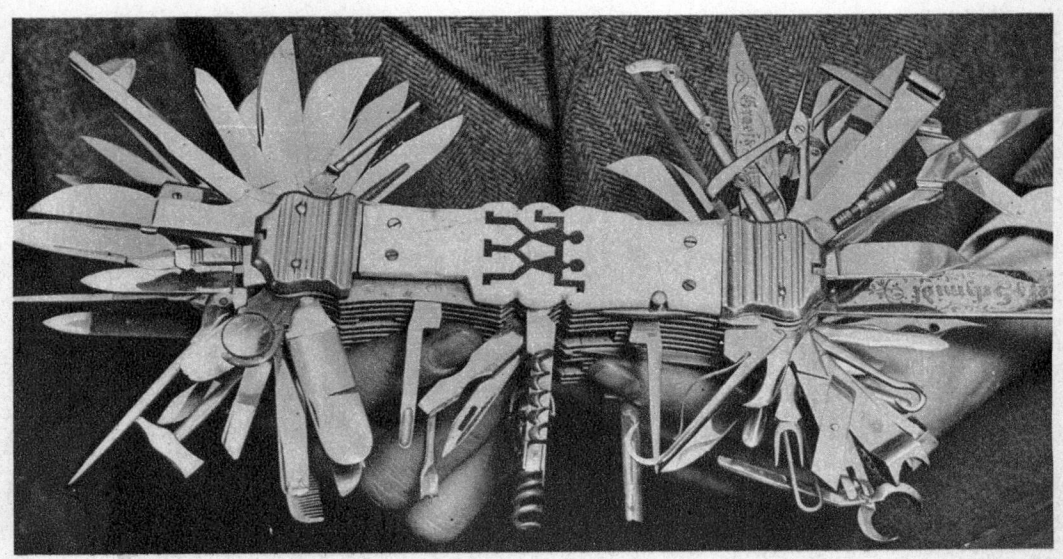

A MARVELOUS KNIFE   Photograph by Underwood and Underwood

PENGUINS

The Strangest Modern Bird

THE penguin, if not the strangest of birds, is at least one of the strangest. They are found only in Antarctic regions. Their capacity to make long sea voyages, yet return to an isolated island to breed, is an outstanding mystery.

Before Columbus Came

FOR several thousand years prior to the time when Columbus came to discover our land, there was relatively high civilization in America. The people who developed and maintained this civilization were not the Indians usually thought of as the "original Americans," but a quite different race known by the name Maya.

The chief seat of Maya civilization about two thousand years before Columbus came was in the region now known as Central America. Much of the territory where agriculture then flourished is now a semi-tropical wilderness—a condition that has enormously hampered the modern archeologist in the attempt to restore the forgotten history of a people for whom the coming of Columbus and his Spanish successors was far from auspicious.

Among the investigators who have braved the discomforts and dangers incident to research at the seat of the Maya civilization is Dr. Herbert J. Spinden, of Harvard University. His efforts have culminated in the apparent establishment of a fixed date—in fact, two fixed dates—in ancient Maya chronology. Systems of Maya chronology had been known, based on monumental records; but until recently there was no way of telling whether the ancient documents were two thousand years old or twice that.

Now, however, the study of certain monuments that were set up in line with the sunrise or sunset points on a certain day of the year, correlated with astronomical and other data, enables Dr. Spinden to establish as the earliest recorded American date the 6th of August, of the year 613 B. C., and as second earliest, the 10th of December, 580 B. C. Whether or not these dates are precisely verified by future investigations, they serve at least to give a general idea of the patriarchal character of the Maya civilization.

At the period in question, abundant records were made in strange hieroglyphics, and a system of measuring time had been devised that is pronounced comparable, or even superior, to any European system. The existence of a system of writing is the recognized test of civilization, lacking which a people must be considered barbarians. The Mayas abundantly meet that test. They were prolific writers, though only three of their books are known to have survived the vandalism of the Spanish conquerors who came in the wake of Columbus.

The Cliff Dwellers of Arizona appear to have occupied an intermediate position in civilization no less than geographically, between the Mayas and the Indians of the North.

Prehistoric American Monuments

THE Maya civilization of Mexico and Central America is only beginning to be revealed to modern archeologists by recent explorations. The new discoveries of ruins of cities in what are now tropical jungles are proving that there was a civilization somewhat comparable to that of ancient India. How these civilized people came to America is one of the outstanding problems of anthropology.

A Natural Monument

THIS strangely poised rock in Yosemite Valley is known as Agassiz Column, in honor of the famous expositor of the glacial theory. This monument represents the work of ice, water, and air, in carving away less resistant parts of a series of geological strata, which were originally tilted at a sharp angle. This is, in fact, the remnant of a former mountainside. It would be hazardous to guess how many years have been required to carve this strange souvenir; but it would be a term measured in million-year units.

IN THE MAYA RUINS

TABLE STONE, USED AS ALTAR, MAYAN CIVILIZATION

Old-Fashioned Heredity

THE casual reader of current scientific literature might be pardoned for getting the idea that the words "heredity" and "Mendelism" are synonymous. It almost seems as if no biologist in recent years had been interested in any non-Mendelian aspect of heredity. There are not a few biologists who feel that practically everything that is worthwhile concerning the subject of inheritance has been acquired since the Mendelian formula was revived.

Such a view, however, is, to say the least, distorted. Mendelism is far from being all of heredity. It is, indeed, doubtful whether the phenomena of Mendelian dominance and recessiveness—the tangibility of which largely accounts for the popularity of the theory — make themselves clearly manifest with regard to any heritable characters except those that are relatively superficial and unimportant. It is characters that are relatively new, in the evolutionary sense, and of minor consequence in the organic scale, that may be juggled with along Mendelian lines. More fundamental characters do not palpably Mendelize.

The original classical experiments of Mendel himself illustrate the point. It will be recalled that he worked with garden peas; and that the groups of characters regarding which he observed the phenomena of dominance and recessiveness were such minor — even if conspicuous—traits as tallness versus shortness of vine, whiteness versus pinkness of blossoms, greenness versus yellowness of pods, smooth versus crinkled peas, and the like. Similarly the experiments that served to establish Mendelism with the modern biologists were largely concerned with the color of hair of domesticated rabbits, rats and guinea pigs; feather colorations of domestic fowls, and the like.

This does not necessarily imply, however, that there may not be inheritance factors for all the more fundamental traits as well, and factors that tend to Mendelize. It may be only that these fundamental traits are so long established and so intricately grouped and correlated that simple experiments do not reveal their relations.

Be that as it may, it is rather gratifying, if for nothing but novelty's sake, to come across such a study as Mr. J. H. Kempton, of the Bureau of Plant Industry, contributes to the *Journal of Heredity*, in which a long series of observations is recorded on the inheritance of a striking anomaly that appears to be transmitted along what might be called old-fashioned lines—that is to say, without obvious deference to the Mendelian hypothesis.

The trait in question consists of the anomaly called "branched ears," in ordinary field corn. The anomaly is apparently of atavistic character, as some types of branched ears have points of resemblance to the seed-head of the Mexican plant called teosinte, from which corn is believed to have been developed. The particular type which is chiefly discussed by Mr. Kempton was discovered in a variety of corn raised by the Pawnee Indians.

The pedigree chart, covering six filial generations, leaves no doubt as to inheritance of the anomaly, but gives no clue to a Mendelian interpretation.

CLIFF DWELLERS, COLORADO

AGASSIZ COLUMN, YOSEMITE VALLEY, CALIFORNIA

Monuments of Steel and Concrete

ONE invention hinges on another. The modern skyscraper could not come into existence until the age of cheap steel and artificial stone, or concrete. Nor could skyscrapers be used as office buildings or as residences, without perfected elevators and the all-essential telephone. So such architectural phenomena as those here shown may be said to typify modern civilization. The tallest structure in the picture is the Chrysler Building, which attained its "highest-ever" height (1046 feet) only to be superseded within a few months by the Empire State Building. There must be a maximum height for such steel and concrete monuments—but no one as yet ventures to say what that maximum may be.

CHRYSLER BUILDING, NEW YORK

INTERNAL COMBUSTION ENGINE

The Gas Engine

MORE technically, and rather more correctly, this is known as the "internal combustion" engine. The principle involved, as regards the piston-thrust, is that of the steam engine. The difference is that the molecules that make the thrust by jostling against one another are made active by the chemical process of ignition within the cylinder. Ignition consists of the union of particles of the original gas with particles of oxygen from the air. Such union takes place initially in the "spark" generated by the electric discharge, and it spreads instantly to the entire gas-content of the cylinder. The perfecting of the gas engine toward the close of the nineteenth century prepared the way for the development of motor-car, Zeppelin, and airplane.

A peculiar problem confronts the gas engine at high altitudes. An ordinary airplane can rise only about 21,000 feet, because the air gets so thin that there is not enough oxygen for the proper feeding of the engine. If greater heights are to be attained, something must be done to feed the engine a condensed-air diet.

To feed it from the oxygen tank which the airman uses would not be feasible, because too much would be required. The alternative is to condense the atmosphere itself by means of a so-called supercharger or "turbo-booster."

The essential part of this apparatus is a set of little propeller blades, like a highly specialized electric fan, driven at enormous speed by the hot exhaust from the airplane motor, and forcing air into a receptacle connected with the carburetors.

Early Types of Gas Engines

LENOIR'S gas engine and the atmospheric gas engine of Otto and Langer are here shown. An atmospheric engine depends on air-pressure to push the piston, a vacuum being produced in the other chamber by condensation of the explosive. Most users of automobiles probably never stop to marvel at the miracles perpetually worked in the cylinders under the hood.

Sky-Writing and Rain-Making

THE method of sky-writing was the invention of a British airman, Captain Cyril Turner. A patented device makes the smoke and expels it directly in the wake of the plane, under control of the pilot. No very exceptional skill is required, it is said, to guide the aerial writing-machine; though, as a matter of course, practise helps. It is predicted that the method will prove a useful means of communication in time of war. In peace-time, it is employed as a new manner of advertising.

The feats of the sky-writer naturally come to mind when one reads of another project that involves the scattering of cloudstuff from an airplane.

The innovators are two Americans, Professor Wilder D. Bancroft, of Cornell University, and Dr. L. Francis Warren. The material sprayed from their airplane is electrified sand; and the object of the maneuver is to induce clouds to give up their moisture in the form of rain.

It is well known that droplets of water in the air form about dust particles. Even the infinitesimal electron may serve as a nucleus of condensation in laboratory experiments. It was hoped that sand particles, charged with positive electricity, might serve to bring about the coalescence of vapor-particles of clouds, to form globules of the order or size of raindrops.

The expectations have been, at least in a measure, verified. Scientific rain-making on a small scale is an accomplished fact. Whether it can be done on a large scale remains to be seen.

ATMOSPHERIC GAS ENGINE

LENOIR'S GAS ENGINE

Water and Gravity in Harness

IT is a familiar but seemingly rather paradoxical principle of hydraulics that the pressure on any given area of surface of a receptacle containing water—be it waterpipe or tank or reservoir or ocean—depends upon the depth of the water and not at all upon its total bulk.

A vivid demonstration of the principle is sometimes made by inserting a piece of small iron pipe into the top of a closed barrel and bursting the barrel by filling the pipe with water.

If the barrel were at the bottom of a vast reservoir (with no support outside its own staves and hoops) it would not burst until the water in the reservoir rose to a certain level; and that level would be found to be just as high above the barrel as the column of water in the inch-pipe used in the other experiment.

But why, it may be asked, does not the pipe burst as well as the barrel? The answer is that the pipe has small aggregate surface. Each square inch of that surface sustains a certain pressure. Each square inch of the barrel sustains the same pressure. The aggregate pressure on the barrel is thus enormously greater than the aggregate pressure on the pipe.

The principle on which the little pipe of water bursts the big barrel is used in the hydraulic press, where a small piston, thrust down with slight force, exerts enormous force on a large piston. The power is multiplied exactly in the ratio of the areas of the two pistons. Here muscular power or steam power, applied through a lever, takes the place of the column of water in the small pipe, merely as a matter of convenience.

An even more familiar practical illustration of the principle is furnished in mountainous regions when water is piped from a lake or reservoir at a height and directed from the nozzle of the pipe against the blades or buckets of a so-called Pelton wheel. A relatively tiny stream of water, with the pressure that gravity has given it, comes against the wheel with the force of a pile-driver.

WOODEN WATER WHEEL OF ANCIENT TYPE

MODERN ALL-STEEL WATER WHEEL

As an example, the recently installed Caribou Hydroelectric plant in California has single water wheels that develop 15,000 horse power under the impact of an eleven-inch jet of water piped from a height of 1,008 feet. The wheel with its accessories weighs more than a hundred tons. The water strikes each successive bucket with an impact of 86,000 pounds. Such is the power of water harnessed with gravity.

A CURRENT MOTOR OR TIDE MACHINE

BEGINNING THE MATCH-MAKING

The Manufacture of Matches

THE "lucifer" match was one of the outstanding marvels of the nineteenth century, and would still be considered an extraordinary thing were it not so familiar. Even so, most users of matches probably know very little about the chemical changes involved when the miracle is performed of making fire with a turn of the wrist. Basically, what happens is that phosphorus, which has the property of combining with oxygen at very low temperatures, is brought in contact with some substance or substances (for example, chlorate of potash) which contain much oxygen and readily give it up. In "safety" matches, the phosphorus is in the rubbing surface, instead of in the head of the match, as in the old-fashioned type of match. The manufacture of wooden matches is highly interesting. It is almost exclusively a machine process. The illustrations are largely self-explanatory, except that it perhaps should be stated that what look like rolls of paper are sheets of veneer, just the thickness of the future match, that have been shaved from the log of wood, revolved against a long blade, in an endless spiral. The veneer is cut to match-length width. The match-sticks projecting from the endless-chain receptacles with scrubbing-brush effect have their tips carried through tanks of paraffin at one place, and at another are brought in contact with the essential chemicals to which they owe their future utility. The finished matches are finally fed into receptacles from which they are taken by hand for packing and shipping.

David's Sling in New Disguise

EVERY boy knows how little David slew Goliath by whirling a stone about his head in a sling, and letting go at just the right moment.

ROLLS OF VENEER

And most boys have practised the art at which David was so proficient, and have acquired at least enough skill to enable them to "come pretty near" hitting such intended targets as wandering dogs and cats, and to break inadvertently a neighbor's window that seemed quite out of range.

The boy who has reached the high-school stage has learned that "centrifugal force" accounts for the extraordinary momentum his sling gave the stone, and has been taught (whether or not he quite understands the explanation) that the incomparable Isaac Newton analyzed the matter and proved that the stone isn't really trying to fly away from the center about which it is whirled, but is merely obeying the law of inertia which impels it to keep up, if permitted to do so, the line of flight in which it finds itself at any given instant.

Practically interpreted, this means that the stone will fly off at a tangent to the circle in which it revolves, if released from a string.

That is just what our earth would do if for an instant the gravitation-pull of the sun were interrupted.

Similarly the moon would divorce itself from the earth and go off on a literal tangent if the gravitation string (strong as a cable of steel miles in thickness) between the two bodies were to be snapped.

If mother earth were to relax her gravitation-hold on the moon at just the right (or wrong) moment, she could send the moon hurtling against old Sol's head on exactly the principle

MATCH-STICKS READY TO BE PARAFFINED

of David's sling, even if not with comparably disastrous results.

Considering the example that David set, it is perhaps rather odd that the principle he used has had little application in modern implements of war.

But now appears an army officer, Major Edward T. Moore, who suggests the making of a David's sling to be whirled about by electrical power and fed with an unending succession of missiles, so that it becomes a noiseless, powderless machine gun sending out two thousand bullets per minute.

He not only suggests this but he has made the apparatus, and demonstrated that it can be used as a weapon with potentialities of terrible destructiveness.

The receptacle into which the bullets are fed rotates ten thousand times per minute. It disgorges two thousand bullets per minute, with initial velocity of about one thousand feet per second—a tornado of death-dealing missiles.

Radio in the Wilderness

RADIO may be helpful in many ways to the city-dweller, but it can never have for him the real meaning that attaches to radio in the wilderness.

Imagine yourself spending the winter in a lumber camp a

CUTTING THE VENEER TO MATCH-LENGTH WIDTH

hundred miles or so from any permanent habitation. Better yet, imagine yourself a lumberjack working month in and month out in a northern logging camp, which you leave at most twice in the year—on Christmas and on the Fourth of July. For months together you are shut out from all physical contact with what we ordinarily speak of as "the world." No newspapers, no letters, no rumors even of what is going on a hundred miles away.

And then imagine that someone installs a radio outfit, so that you can listen nightly to the news of what is happening all over the world, and to concerts and lectures. You are no longer isolated. You are up to the minute in your knowledge of affairs.

Then radio becomes something more than a divertissement.

This is just what has happened in many lumber communities. Away out in the forests of the Coast Range in Oregon and Washington, the Hammond Lumber Company has installed powerful receiving sets in more than twenty of the logging camps. The lumberjacks listen in on San Francisco and Portland and Seattle, and never lack for entertainment.

Sky Temperatures

TO a good many people, it seems paradoxical that the temperature is lower up in the sky, with the sun right above you, than it is at the surface of the earth. The explanation, of course, is that it is not the direct rays of the sun during any

MATCHES FOR PACKING

given hour that chiefly determine the general temperature of the day—else it would always be hottest just at noon, and the hottest day of the year in the northern hemisphere would always be the day of the summer solstice, on or about June 21. That such is not the case is due to the absorption of heat by land and water, and its subsequent radiation under changing atmospheric conditions.

The atmosphere itself forms a blanket about the earth, preventing very rapid radiation; the degree of protection it affords being modified from hour to hour by the relative amount of water vapor it contains.

RUNNING THE MATCH-HEADS THROUGH THE CHEMICAL TANKS

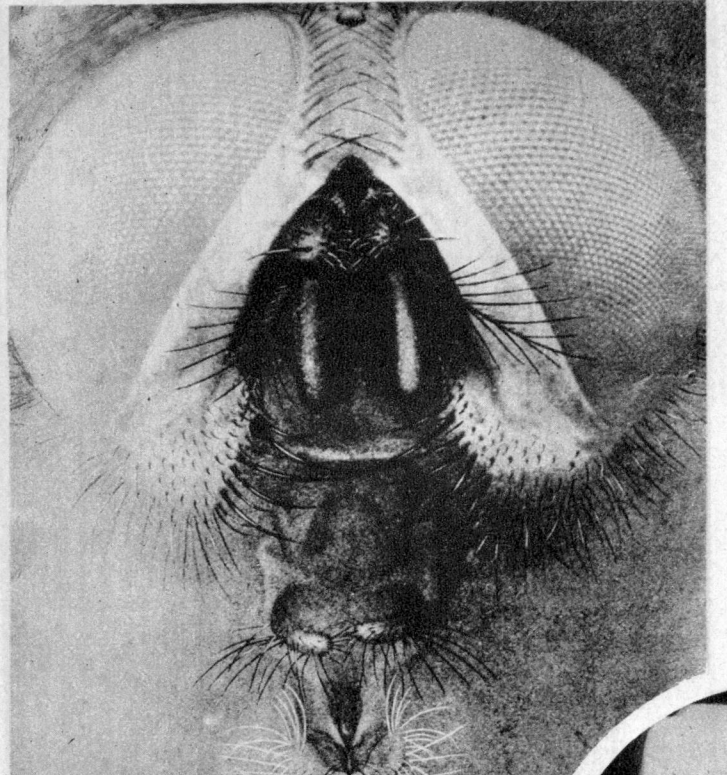

HEAD OF HOUSE FLY

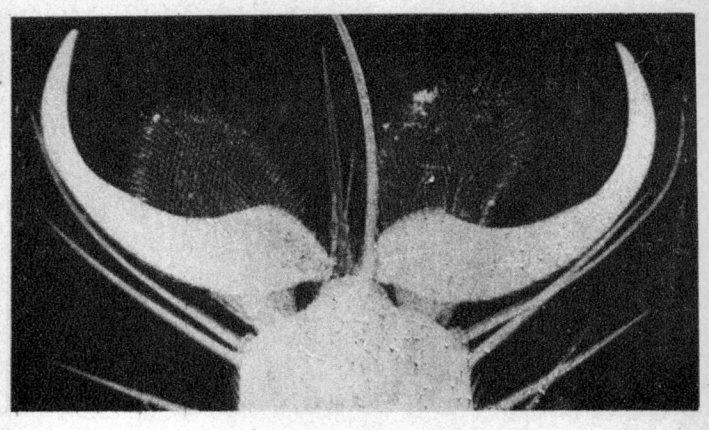

FLY'S FOOT

HUMAN HAND PHOTOGRAPHED FROM IMAGE IN FLY'S EYE

COMMON FLY

Our Enemy the House Fly

AN astonishing and alarming creature, the fly, when magnified so that the true form of his head, feet, tongue, and body in general are clearly visible. The amazing multiple eye is perhaps the most astonishing feature of all. Every one of the myriad facets of the eye mirrors the surroundings. The human hand here shown was directly photographed from the image in one facet of a fly's eye. There were thousands of closely similar images in the multiple eye. From the two-eyed standpoint of the human observer, this might seem likely to be confusing, but the fly does not seem to find it so.

Humanity and the Fly

THE fly has been lauded as a scavenger, and not without reason.

But presently it occurred to someone that a scavenger that comes directly to the dinner table from scavenging, without washing its hands, was not precisely an esthetic companion.

And then tests were made that proved that bacteria of sundry tribes, including thoroughly noxious ones, were carried about on the fly's perambulators; and the real utility of the little insect was at last revealed; its mission is to aid materially in preventing the world from becoming overpopulated with human beings. And to that end it has worked effectively.

As the carrier of germs of typhoid fever alone it has doubtless accomplished more in that direction than all the predacious mammals in existence, including warlike man himself.

Can you and I, as individuals or as members of a community, do anything really worth while toward reducing the fly population?

That depends. If you are a city dweller, perhaps you cannot personally do much. You must depend on your Board of Health.

But if you live in a village or a suburb, you can probably do a great deal. By "swatting" every fly you encounter? Well, there is no harm in that. It is a good enough beginning. And you may reflect that the killing of one fly in the early part of the season may be equivalent to the destruction of whole swarms in the late summer; for, if undisturbed, the insects multiply with almost unbelievable rapidity.

The statistics are fairly stupefying, the potential progeny of a single female, if unchecked, in a summer season, running into thirty figures! (We are assured that twelve generations totally unrestrained, if food could be found, would outbulk the earth itself.)

Properly dispose of all refuse and decaying matter, vegetable and animal, and there will remain no place for the fly to deposit her eggs with any prospect of food for the young maggots that represent the new generation. And that, of course, would mean race suicide.

Fighting Fleas and Ticks

A NEW era in preventive medicine dates from the discovery, made by Dr. Theobald Smith, that a suctorial insect may inoculate its victim with the germs of a contagious disease. The malady studied by Dr. Smith was Texas cattle fever. The guilty insect was a species of tick. If the insects are destroyed, by making their bovine hosts swim through a tank of germicidal oil, an infected animal may mingle with others without spreading the disease.

A British physician showed that the germs of malaria are conveyed by a mosquito. American physicians, working in Cuba, proved that another mosquito is the carrier of the germ of yellow fever.

It became known that the rat flea is the carrier of the germs of Asiatic plague, and the tsetse fly the disseminator of sleeping sickness. The tribe of ticks achieved further unenviable notoriety as carriers of germs of various maladies, including the dreaded "spotted fever," or mountain fever.

The woodtick that spreads mountain fever selects various animal hosts, including rabbits and ground squirrels, passing from these animals on occasion to a human victim. The bite of the tick is not in itself deadly, but it may become so if the insect has ingested the germs of mountain fever. For the spread of this dangerous malady the woodtick is responsible.

No available method of exterminating the tick presents itself. At least three medical investigators have lost their lives in attempting to solve the problem of restricting the malady to its present locus or banishing it altogether.

Physicians of the United States Public Health Service are attacking the problem by endeavoring to develop an immunizing serum, with which to give protection against development of the malady.

The great desideratum is a method of destroying the woodtick tribe. Whoever devises such a method will be a public benefactor.

FLEA FIGHTERS

RAT FIGHTERS

Genius and a Meat Diet

A ONCE famous story records that enemies of General Grant brought word to President Lincoln, after Vicksburg, that the commander had been under the influence of liquor at the time of the battle. Lincoln is represented as responding: "Find out for me what brand of whisky he used, so that I can supply it to my other generals."

This story comes naturally to mind when one reads the statement that Charles Darwin's mental peculiarities are being interpreted by a modern physiologist as due to a thyroid disturbance in connection with a meat diet.

THE BOOK OF MARVELS

For, of course, the heat that comes directly from the sun supplies precisely the same kind of energy that we liberate by burning coal; and if we had sufficient ingenuity we could hitch our machinery to the sunbeams directly instead of through the roundabout channel of the coal mines.

The only trouble is that the heat of sunlight is so diffused that there is not enough of it at any one point to do a great deal of work. There is need of concentration. With lens or concave mirror you can bring a shaft of sunlight to focus and start a fire or boil a test-tube of water.

Why not use a big lens or a big concave mirror to bring many shafts of sunlight to a focus and thus make a big fire or boil a large receptacle of water?

The big lens is too expensive; but a concave mirror of indefinite size may be cheaply made by putting together small panes of glass, and so a large amount of sunlight may be brought to a focus. This has been done in a machine shown in the illustration. A long parabolic mirror throws its focused light on the water pipe running down its center, with the heating power of a furnace. Any kind of machinery may be hitched to it.

It is plausibly predicted that the time will come when sun engines, more or less like this, will be set up in regions that now are arid, because they are cloudless, and that the desert spaces of to-day will thus become the great manufacturing centers of tomorrow. When that time comes the center of old-world civilization will perhaps oscillate back to Northern Africa, and our own "great American desert" may exceed in populousness and fertility the Mississippi Valley as it is to-day.

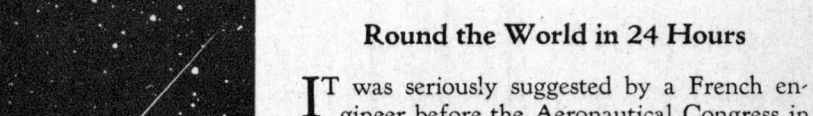

A TRANSIT INSTRUMENT

Using a Transit Instrument

THIS is a telescope so mounted that it rotates only in one plane—the north and south plane, or meridian. Its chief use is to determine the exact instant when a given star crosses the meridian. The field of the transit instrument is likely to have a crossed spider web at its center, to make observation exact. The observer presses an electric button at the instant when transit is observed; but since the nervous system does not operate instantaneously, and since the reactions of different people differ, there is an element called the "personal equation" to be used in checking the results attained by each individual observer.

A METEOR

Round the World in 24 Hours

IT was seriously suggested by a French engineer before the Aeronautical Congress in Paris that it might soon be possible to fly from Paris to Paris via the Atlantic Ocean, the American continent, the Pacific Ocean, and Asia in twenty-four hours.

The suggestion seems fantastic, until we reflect that the earth turns clear round in the time suggested. And the thought emerges that if one were able to go above the air and hold oneself stationary there, the surface of the earth would whirl by so that one would in effect journey westward at the rate of something like a thousand miles an hour.

A Meteor Entering the Earth's Atmosphere

METEORS are minute fragments of world-stuff that enter the earth's atmosphere by millions, and are heated to incandescence by atmospheric friction, and hence made visible. Mostly they are turned to gas in a few seconds at longest. Occasionally a larger fragment reaches the earth's surface. It is then called a meteorite.

Sunlight in Place of Coal

PARADOXICALLY enough, we dig into the earth laboriously to extract coal, which has been described as "bottled sunlight," while we ignore the original article itself, which exists in unlimited supply above ground. Subsequent generations will doubtless regard this as a convincing evidence of twentieth century stupidity.

SUNLIGHT IN PLACE OF COAL

The difficulty is that in going into the air we carry the earth's momentum with us, and that even the swiftest airplane, flying westward, can neutralize only a small fraction of this momentum. But now it is suggested that if an airplane were to rise—with the aid of the turbo-booster for condensing air—to an altitude of eight or ten miles, the atmospheric resistance would be so slight that the flying machine might presently attain a speed comparable to that of the earth's rotation. Then, of course, the round-the-world journey becomes feasible.

The thing might be done just as well near the earth were it not for atmospheric resistance.

The present writer long ago suggested the theoretical feasibility of the twenty-four-hour airplane journey round the world. It is interesting to observe that professional aviators are now giving the problem attention.

Planetarium for Popular Exposition of Astronomy

THE apparatus projects images of sun, moon, planets, and stars upon the canvas dome of the new Adler Planetarium building, at Chicago. A notable educational device. People nowadays get their information at the movie theater. Thousands will marvel at the artificial firmament who never think to look up at the actual sky.

PROJECTOR OF ADLER PLANETARIUM

THE ADLER PLANETARIUM

An Artificial Horizon for the Navigator

THE reflecting surface is held in the horizontal plane by gyroscopic action. The inventor was Elmer E. Sperry, whose gyroscopic stabilizer for the airplane and gyro-compass for ships made him famous.

Ventilation for Health

THE doctrine that fresh air and plenty of it, day and night, summer and winter, makes for health has become an article of faith with most hygienists.

The doctrine has found support in the practical experience of sanitariums for tuberculosis in particular; and the out-of-door sleeping porch has been heralded as a health-builder and life-saver.

The doctrine is alluring, and on its face plausible, considering the systemic need of oxygen. Yet it has not gone quite unchallenged.

THE SPERRY GYROSCOPIC HORIZON

It has been suggested, for example, that the coldness of the air rather than its mere freshness gives it value (through stimulating formation of blood corpuscles) in the Adirondack sanitariums; and a prominent naturalist, who has spent much time in the open, has even propounded the heresy that too much ventilation may be positively detrimental to health, and the direct cause of many a premature death.

A view so unorthodox serves at least to call attention to the fact that our knowledge of ventilation as bearing on human health is for the most part empirical.

Recent experiments in which carbonic acid gas is used in the treatment of tuberculosis tend further to set one thinking along new lines, and it becomes fairly evident that it would be well to have definite information about a good many aspects of the problem of ventilation that hitherto have been rather taken for granted even by thoughtful people.

The tests are conducted in an airtight chamber lined with four inches of cork, into which air of varying quality is piped.

Predetermined and carefully controlled and recorded variations as to chemical composition, temperature, moisture and rate of change of the air are coordinated with observed bodily changes of the human subjects within the chamber.

Pulse rate, blood pressure, and bodily temperature—surface and internal—are among the physiological processes under observation.

FORMER TIMBER LAND

One Way to Banish a Forest

EIGHT years before this picture was made the trees of the forest were girdled, and of course died. The leafless trunks permitted enough sunlight to reach the soil for maintenance of plant growth. The forest became a cornfield and then a pasture. Ultimately the dead trees will be removed. The soil is rich, and the roots of the trees protect it in large measure from erosion.

Morning Eagle Falls

THIS beautiful waterfall is in Glacier National Park, Montana. The photograph gives an impressive view of the rock-formation, not only of the cliff over which the water flows, but of the "mesas" or table mountains in the background. Observe that the strata are nearly horizontal, showing that the entire region was lifted from its original sea-bed position to the present elevation practically without tipping. A level plateau was thus formed, from which the present mountains have been carved by erosion of water and sand-bearing wind.

© 1912, Kiser Photo Co.
MORNING EAGLE FALLS

London to Tokyo in Four Days

NOT this month, to be sure, probably not this year, but at some time not so very far in the future, it is confidently predicted, the tourist will be able to step aboard ship—meaning airship, of course—at London for a four-day voyage at the end of which he will come to earth at Tokyo, in far-away Japan. And he will have traveled only 6,080 miles; less than half the distance of the shortest steamship route between the same ports, which is by way of the Panama Canal, and is accomplished in thirty-five days. Theoretically, at least, the airship could make four round trips in that time.

This is on the assumption that the airship route lies along the line of the "great circle" between London and Tokyo, and that the craft does not deviate from this shortest possible course.

Observation of an ordinary map, which shows the Polar regions swollen to equatorial dimensions, does not prepare one to understand why such a project should receive a moment's consideration. On such a map, the air-line route between London and Tokyo seems to cross Newfoundland, Nova Scotia, and a large section of the United States, just about midway between Alaska and the Panama Canal. A London-Nome-Tokyo route seems almost rectangular. The selection of such a route seems about as logical as if one were to include Toronto, Canada, in a supposedly direct route between New York and St. Louis.

But a glance at a school globe or at the Cahill Butterfly map solves the mystery, making it evident that the Polar region is the natural airway between western Europe and eastern Asia. More than that, it appears that the Polar route is the route of choice between northern Europe and our own Pacific coast. From Stockholm to San Francisco via the Arctic is but 5,250 miles; whereas the distance is 7,400 miles if you make the journey "directly" by steamship from Stockholm to New York and then by rail straight across our country to the Pacific city.

The Last Throes of a Geyser

THIS spectacular photograph of the old Excelsior geyser has peculiar interest, because in recent years this marvelous natural fountain has ceased to operate. The extinction of so extraordinary a "spouter" is hardly less thought-provocative than its operation. What are the changes taking place in the lower regions of the earth's crust that can obliterate so prodigious a waterspout? There is no clear answer.

EXCELSIOR GEYSER, NOW EXTINCT

An Extraordinary Natural Mirror

PERHAPS it is the photograph, by the Kiser Photo Company, of Portland, Oregon, that is extraordinary, rather than the mirror, which after all is like any other lake surface, where the water is uncontaminated, in a time of absolute calm. From another viewpoint, however, perfect duplication of any object by reflection is an extraordinary phenomenon. It implies a surface of exceeding smoothness. To make such a surface is a mechanical accomplishment of high order—as you may learn by asking anyone who has ground the mirror of a reflecting telescope. Nature makes a smooth water surface, when the atmosphere can be quieted, through the operation of gravitation, aided by the cohesive force that gives surface tension between molecules in the plane of contact between two mediums of different density. This is done so well that the suggestion has been made that a gigantic telescope could perhaps utilize a shallow pool of liquid mercury, revolved just fast enough to give it appropriate concavity. So far as I know, practical test has not been made of the project.

© 1909, Kiser Photo Co.

A NATURAL MIRROR

A Strange Crustacean

THE mother lobster is a very notable egg-producer. She is believed to spawn only every other year, but she begins very young and her clutch of eggs varies from about 3,000 as a minimum to a maximum of something like 75,000. There is no suggestion of race suicide in that sort of productivity, but the very fact of such fecundity tells of a terrific struggle for existence. And in reality millions of young lobsters fall prey to the fish enemies that abound in their habitat.

The eggs go through a singularly long period of incubation, about ten months, during which time they are carried by the mother as a sort of apron glued to the under side of her body. During this period the mother lobster is said to be "in berry," and she cannot legally be taken for the market; but fishermen are not unduly careful in regarding the prohibition and predacious fish regard it not at all, finding the egg-encumbered mother a relatively easy victim.

When the eggs hatch, the mother lobster is freed from further parental duties. The young are free-swimming creatures that float about near the surface of the water for several weeks, during that time undergoing four molts, or changes of skin—provided they have the luck to escape the schools of surface-feeding fish against which they have virtually no protection.

After the fourth molt, the young lobster begins to look like a lobster—and to develop the propensity to seek the bottom of the water. Snuggling and burrowing there, he evades his enemies if he can, and feasts on almost anything in the way of food that comes to hand. The hard protective shell will not change in size, so from time to time he splits it along the back and comes out of it, improving the opportunity to grow while the new shell is hardening.

A STRANGE CRUSTACEAN

Safety at Sea

AN iceberg or a derelict floats across the course; a fog settles; there is direct or glancing impact with shock that no man-made structure could resist—and in an instant the question of emergency equipment assumes a new aspect.

No longer are the lifeboats to be regarded as supernumerary decorations. And there are never lifeboats enough.

The old-fashioned life preserver is little better than an instrument of torture if the wearer must remain long in the cold water; hence one looks with special interest upon a curious substitute recently invented—a collapsible float operated like an inverted umbrella and said to be unsinkable when inflated.

It is, in effect, a circular boat, said to be able to hold two or three persons in still water, and to be safe for one person in the roughest sea; yet when collapsed it is a mere bag, readily carried in the hand.

CRATER LAKE NATIONAL PARK

Crater Lake

WATER has accumulated in an ancient crater to form a lake without tangible inlet or outlet. Evaporation, however, keeps the water at approximately the same level for a prolonged period—in ordinary terms. Lakes do not as a rule persist for a long period, in geological reckoning. Ordinary lakes result from the stopping up of a valley-outlet, through deposit of detritus. Glacial action accounts for most lakes of the northern part of our continent. Eventually, changes of level and contour of the land surface give the lake new outlets. It is predicted, for example, that Lake Michigan will some day discharge to the southwest, across Illinois. Sediment accumulating in the bottom of such a lake as this will finally cause it to overflow, or fill up the hollow altogether. In contrast to lakes, rivers are very persistent features of the landscape, though shifting the exact line of flow.

PETS THAT ARE DIFFERENT

Why Teach Children to Be Afraid?

THIS little girl is evidently enjoying herself playing with snakes. Yet most children, placed under similar conditions, would be thrown into spasms of terror; and comparatively few adults can observe even the photographs without experiencing a feeling of repugnance.

How are we to explain the anomaly? Simply enough. The child of the photographs has never been taught to be afraid.

As she sits there absorbed in the game of snake-festooning, she is quite unconsciously teaching a great lesson in pedagogics that every parent should take to heart.

She is proving that fears which appear to be almost universal with men and women are not necessarily "instinctive," as we are commonly taught, but have been acquired, just as we acquire most other mental and moral traits.

You and I are afraid of snakes—shrinking from even so harmless and beautiful a creature as the little garter snake gliding through the grass—not because our arboreal ancestors were attacked by gigantic serpents but because in our early childhood we observed some adult manifesting fear or repugnance at sight either of an actual serpent or of the picture of one, perhaps in a child's story book.

The receptive mind of the child—"wax to receive and marble to retain"—gained instantly an impression that became the foundation for a lifelong aversion.

A good share of the fears, aversions and prejudices that hamper our lives had a similar origin.

The average parent uses imaginary "bears" and "goblins" and bugaboos of sundry varieties as means of discipline or amusement, and then wonders that the child grows into a cowardly, superstitious or even morally perverted adult. Seldom is it realized that a quite different personality might have been developed by a different childhood training.

That, however, is the highly important lesson that the child who is unafraid of snakes is forcefully teaching.

The Strangest Animal in America

IF the entire animal population of our continent were to march in procession up Broadway, let us say, and a popular vote were taken as to which animal is the strangest of them all, there can be little doubt that the armadillo would receive the blue ribbon.

It would be admitted that the pouch-bearing opossum, the quill-covered hedgehog, and the airplane-winged bat are queer creatures. But the palm for oddity would go to the little beast that is encased in a well-fitting suit of almost impenetrable bony armor, ingeniously jointed to allow flexibility of motion while giving complete protection against its ordinary enemies.

It might be thought that a wearer of armor would be a militant creature, but such is not the case. The little armadillo wears the bony casement not because it intends to take the offensive against other animals, but solely as protection against the various predacious beasts and birds that might otherwise find it an easy victim. Practically its sole defense when attacked it to roll itself up into a ball. But that is quite defense enough, inasmuch as the ball is composed of the horny covering that tooth and talon of the enemy cannot penetrate.

The armadillo's only other effective answer to an attack is to burrow into

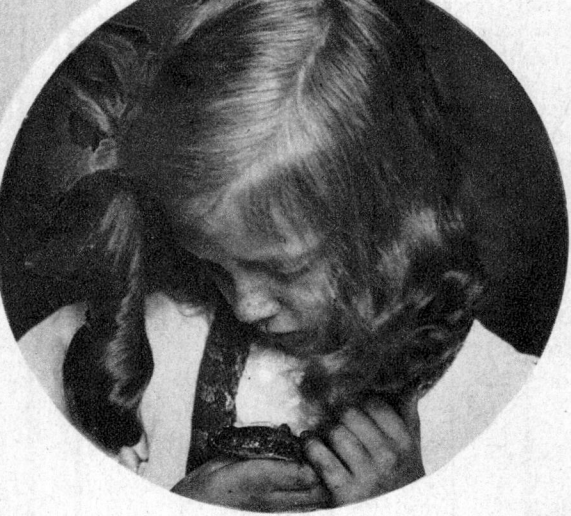

FRIENDS

OPOSSUM

BAT

the earth, which it does with great expeditiousness, on occasion. When foraging on its own account, it attacks nothing larger than the ant, which forms its chief article of diet.

When we speak of anything as "strange" we mean, of course, merely that it is "different." The armor-bearing armadillo is strange merely because most other beasts wear hair instead of bony plates on their outsides. But, strangeness aside, the little creature has peculiar interest as illustrating one of nature's experiments in giving an animal protection against its enemies without supplying it either with speedy legs or the capacity to fight.

About Chromosomes

IT appears that various species of fruit flies (*Drosophila*) are susceptible of being reared with great ease in captivity; that they are exceedingly prolific, and of such short span of life that many successive generations may be studied in a term of months. Meantime it chances that the chromosomes of the dividing cells of these insects are so few in number and of such distinct patterns as to make them ideal for study under the microscope.

What, then, is a chromosome? The answer is that a chromosome is a minute structure within a living cell which has been

PORCUPINE

ARMADILLO

proved to be the carrier of hereditary characteristics from parent to offspring. There are definite numbers of chromosomes in the cells of any given species of living creature, and the little thread-like structures are arranged in definite and characteristic formations with almost diagrammatic clearness.

All this, to be sure, is known chiefly through study of cells that have ceased to be alive, and that have been stained with anilin dyes, so that the chromosomes become sharply visible. Etymologically, the word chromosome means "colored body," and it was applied originally because these little structures—fortunately for the biologist—take a much deeper stain than the other portions of the cell, and thus are revealed, when viewed under high powers of the microscope, as dark figures against a lighter background.

No fewer than thirteen types of chromosome groups are known for different species of fruit flies. Many species are represented by the same type, but no two species have chromosome-groups of exactly the same individual pattern. Cases are recorded in which the different species of flies are so similar in appearance and habit that they were supposed to be identical until the microscope had shown a difference of chromosomes. And the microscopic finding was verified by observing that the two types could not interbreed.

THE BOOK OF MARVELS

AFTER IRRIGATION

BEFORE IRRIGATION

IRRIGATION DITCH IN WASHINGTON

IRRIGATED ORCHARD IN OREGON

The Magic Power of Water

ABSENCE of water makes a desert. The soil of the desert may be exceedingly rich in plant foods. But, lacking moisture, plants cannot grow. Much of the land of the "Great American Desert" of the southwestern United States is barren simply because the mountain ranges west of it cause precipitation of the rain that they need, and the water is carried off to the Pacific without serving its normal purpose. The proof that the soil is rich is furnished when the streams are dammed and the desert land is fed through irrigation canals. The aforetime desert then becomes a garden or a wheatfield, at option of the irrigator, as these photographs demonstrate. Note the two companion photographs that show the same landscape before and after using.

Migration Mysteries

ARMED with the compass, sextant, and charts, the navigator is able to make his way across the ocean and into a designated port with a certainty that always seems astonishing to the landsman.

The methods that he uses, however, are quite intelligible, and, once the principles are mastered, even simple.

But there is a type of navigation performed without compass or sextant which is a matter of familiar observation but which nevertheless remains utterly mysterious. I refer to the journeys made by such navigators as migratory birds, fish of the salmon tribe, and animals like the fur-seal.

When a golden plover flies by night from Nova Scotia to Brazil, or when a salmon comes out of the depths of the sea and arrives with certainty at the mouth of, let us say, the Columbia River, or when a fur-seal makes a journey of a thousand miles or two and reaches the shores of a little island lost in the North Pacific—there is cause for astonishment.

No one knows how such feats are accomplished. They lie entirely beyond the capacity of any human navigator. To say that the bird and fish and mammal are guided by "instinct" is merely to hide behind a word. Some tangible guide-posts there must be in air or water or ether of which the human perception takes no cognizance; but as to their character, we are still in total ignorance.

Feathered Artists

THE nest of the Baltimore oriole is a graceful cradle, suspended from slender twigs; composed of a veritable textile, so deftly woven as to challenge belief that such a work of art could be produced without hands and with no weaving apparatus except the bill of a bird.

A human artist would find it hard, indeed, to duplicate this curious fabric, woven of shreds of wool-like plant fiber and strips of bark and horsehair, and made into a piece of cloth so stout that your utmost effort cannot tear it.

It is of peculiar interest to note that this wonderful fabric which the oriole shapes into a nest has always the same general appearance, whether fashioned in New England or in Iowa.

Yet there may be diversity of practise among different builders as to the relative amount of horsehair and strips of bark utilized, and in particular as to the proportion of fragments of twine incorporated with the other materials.

The nest here shown is woven exclusively of man-made materials. The second picture shows the very deep nest of a related tropical species.

All in all, we have a structure remarkable not merely for its texture but for its location.

Almost no other small bird is able to build its nest in the treetops; because the others have not the artistry to swing a cradle from the tips of the twigs, which alone gives safety.

Of our hundreds of species of birds, the vireos alone vie with the oriole in making pensile nests; but even they seldom build in the treetops.

Birds That Are Different

THE habit of brooding the eggs and caring for the young during their period of immaturity is so characteristic of birds that one naturally thinks of it as a distinctively avian trait.

The classifiers divide birds into two great groups: one comprising those that run about soon after coming out of the shell (Precoces), the other those that remain for some time in the nest (Altrices).

But the precocial youngsters, no less than the nestlings, receive careful attention from the mother bird (and often from the father as well) until they have attained a measure of practical experience and advanced toward maturity.

One need go no farther afield than the barnyard to note how fondly chickens and ducklings and goslings are mothered.

About the dooryard, in nesting time, may be seen robins and chirping sparrows and wrens and bluebirds, to name only a few of the most familiar species, whose parental solicitude for their fledglings finds almost frenzied expression.

No one having the slightest acquaintance with birds of the dooryard or those of field and woodland can question that the maternal instinct is profoundly developed in the feathered race.

And yet there are two well-known birds that depart utterly

ORIOLE'S NEST BUILT AT HOME OF ANOTHER

TROPICAL ORIOLE'S NEST

from the traditions of the race, and never under any circumstances make nests or brood eggs or care for their young.

These birds are the European cuckoo and the American cowbird.

The two species are quite unrelated in the eye of the taxonomist. They are not classified even in the same order. They are totally different in appearance and in general habit and habitat.

The sole point of resemblance is that each has developed the anomalous habit of laying its eggs in the nests of other birds, leaving the business of brooding them and caring for the future fledglings solely to the foster parent.

In each case the nest selected by the unnatural mother as cradle for her offspring is that of a smaller bird.

A common victim of the cowbird is the yellow warbler. The involuntary hostess seldom seems to observe the intrusion, though I once knew a warbler to build a second floor in its nest, burying the unwelcome egg.

As a rule, nidification follows the normal course; and presently the cowbird fledgling manages to oust the smaller rightful occupants from the nest, securing for itself the exclusive attention of the poor little dupe upon whom it has been foisted.

How so strange a reversal of instincts has become operative in case of two birds among thousands is one of the outstanding puzzles of natural history.

Tides and Storms

THE rolling of sea waves in a calm is in part due to tidal influence—the tides being caused by the gravitational pull between the earth and the moon and sun. Tides on opposite sides of the earth follow the moon (lagging a little), and so rise and fall twice daily, since the earth makes a complete revolution in 24 hours. The tidal effect influences the crust of the earth as well as the water, but of course the solid crust moves only a fraction as much as the ocean surface. The tidal pull is greatest when the sun and moon are in line on the same side of the earth, and so pull together. Big ocean waves are the combined result of tidal influence and the winds. The waves in a storm seem to race with the wind, but in reality their movement is largely oscillatory. Local masses of water rise and fall, and do not rush ahead as they seem to do. Winds are due to changes in temperature of regions of the earth's surface, combined with the rotation of the earth itself. In general, cool air from the polar regions flows toward the equator at a lower level, and hot air from the equatorial region flows poleward overhead, in compensation. As air retains for a time the eastward momentum of the region from which it comes, the poleward currents have an easterly trend. All large masses of air in motion take on a rotary or cyclonic motion. It appears that all bodies in space, large or small, take on a rotary motion—from atoms to suns and galaxies. No very satisfactory explanation of this familiar phenomenon has ever been given. The first law of motion (every body tends to maintain its state of rest or movement) explains why the earth continues to spin, once started, but the start is not fully explained.

HURRICANE AT SEA

MODERN TOWER OF BABEL

Modern Towers of Babel

UNLIKE the traditional builders of the tower of the elder day, the modern architects have not been confounded, but have accomplished their tasks of sky-piercing with astonishing precision and celerity. They have produced structures representing a new type of architecture, designed to give the greatest possible floor space above the small available ground space. These structures, dwarfing the highest buildings of antiquity, would have been accounted super-wonders of the world in the day when the relatively diminutive "Colossus" at Rhodes counted as one of the seven major wonders. The Empire State Building at the left is the tallest building ever erected prior to the year 1932. Height, 1248 feet.

Testing Would-Be High-Fliers

OF the multitudinous obstacles that stood in the way of the pioneer workers in the field of aviation, one of the most curious was the belief, entertained apparently by many men of science, that human beings could not safely venture to sever physical connection with the earth's surface.

Even after animals had been sent up in balloons and had come down unscathed, men still hesitated. The Montgolfier brothers, first successful makers of balloons, refused to make personal test of the man-carrying quality of their invention, and the hazardous experiment was about to be made with two condemned criminals, reprieved from the guillotine for the purpose, when a brave man named Rozier came forward and offered to risk his own life rather than see "vile criminals" accorded the glory of being the first to ascend into the air.

Rozier's hazardous feat consisted of ascending to the height of eighty feet in a captive balloon and remaining there for a few minutes. Not a remarkable performance, assuredly, in the modern view; but the first attempt of its kind, marking an epoch in the history of man's conquest of the air.

All this occurred in the year 1783, and with the use of the hot-air balloon. At a later day, however, with the advent of the hydrogen-filled balloon, as men flew higher and higher, they discovered that there is, after all, a measure of justification for the fears of the early physiologists; for breathing conditions are by no means the same in the upper air that they are at the earth's surface. Modern science explains the difference readily enough, to be sure; it is merely a matter of the thinning out of the atmosphere, with attendant reduction of the oxygen supply.

In very recent years, since high-flying has become a military profession, it has been found that individual aviators differ materially in their resistance to the enervating effects of changed atmospheric conditions at high altitudes. Some men are physiologically unfitted for high flying. In rarified atmosphere their senses become blunted, they lose the power of quick response, or they become dazed or partially unconscious.

If a man is thus handicapped by nature, it is obviously desirable that his disability should be known without testing it by actual ascent to hazardous altitudes. So methods have been devised whereby the atmospheric conditions at any altitude may be duplicated in a caisson; air of modified temperature and oxygen-content being supplied the would-be aviators through gas masks, and various instruments of precision recording the results of reaction-tests.

With the Fish for Model

THIS so-called Whaleback steamship is of a type popular on the Great Lakes, notably for the transportation of iron ore from the Lake Superior region to the Lake Erie docks from which it is shipped to Pittsburgh. The advantages of such a craft in rough weather are obvious. They are built for stability, of course; but the whale furnishes an excellent speed-model as well. The original model for speed craft, in water or air, was the fish. The practical perfection of the model is demonstrated by the fact that when, in the course of geologic time, marine reptiles and then mammals were evolved, each in turn adopted the fish-form. Ultimately, man discovered, first by practical tests, and then by laboratory experiments, that this model—blunt nose and tapering stern—is the form best adapted for "streamline" effects. It appears that air or water, flowing about the bow of such a craft, actually curves around and pushes forward on the afterpart of the hull. The motor-boat with flat bottom, designed to skim along the top of the water, is the only speed-craft that departs from the model.

SPEED MODEL

WHALEBACK SHIP

To Rescue the Drowning

A NOVEL type of life-saving apparatus has been devised, which, if generally adopted, should considerably reduce the mortality from drowning at summer resorts.

It consists of two air-filled tubes or floats that come together in front like the prow of a boat, to which a framework is attached that supports a pair of pedals like those of a bicycle.

The pedals operate a propeller like that of an ordinary motor-boat.

A bizarre, nondescript contraption when seen out of water, but light enough to be carried readily by one man.

Placed in the water, the apparatus becomes a float that can be propelled by leg-power of the operator much faster than anyone can swim.

Its prow, lying just at the surface of the water, has a piece of canvas stretched across it, forming a support on which the body of a drowning person may easily be pulled without danger to the rescuer.

The entire maneuver of rescuing a drowning person might be effected by a novice who is himself unable to swim.

Here, then, is an apparatus of obvious utility, so simple of construction that it could be made by any mechanic of average skill, once the idea is grasped.

The original mechanism may be patented, for aught I know to the contrary, but that would not prevent anyone from imitating it in making a life-saver for personal use.

BATTLESHIP OF THE SEVENTEENTH CENTURY

RECEIVING CABLEGRAM

The Morse Telegraph

TELEGRAPHY is too familiar a present-day practise to excite even interest, let alone wonder. But about a century ago, when Samuel F. B. Morse demonstrated the possibility of sending verbal messages by electricity, his invention created as much excitement and wonderment as any new scientific achievement before or afterward. And, rightly considered, the telegraph is a marvel of marvels to-day, in the ultimate sense inexplicable, since no one knows precisely how and why an electric "current" flows. Our pictures show the original Morse instrument and the newest type of cablegram receiver.

The New Niagara Colossus

ONE of the greatest inventions of all time is the water wheel. No one knows where or when it was developed, but its use dates from remote antiquity, and it continued to be far and away the most important of inanimate workers until the advent of the steam engine, late in the eighteenth century. To the craftsmen of the early day, it must have seemed an ideal force-developer. It was almost absurdly simple of construction, and it supplied power in the form of rotary motion. You had simply to adjust a belt to the axle of the wheel, and it would set any kind of machinery in motion.

There were two familiar ways of adjusting the primitive water wheel. It might be placed above a current of running water, so that the blades barely dipped into the stream at the lower part of their revolution, constituting an "undershot" wheel; or it might be placed below a dam, so that the water would fall on the blades at the upper part of their revolution, constituting an "overshot" wheel. In either case, the wheel was set spinning by the impact of water that would never cease flowing while the supply lasted. Gravitation never tires, and nothing ever goes wrong with it.

Viewing the subject in retrospect, in the light of the excellent hindsight with which we are all endowed, it seems rather strange that no practical use was made of a third type of water wheel, now familiar as the turbine, until modern times. It is true that the turbine seems less rudimentarily simple than the other water wheels, but the principle on which it operates was perfectly familiar throughout the ages because it is utilized in the operation of another equally primitive device, the windmill. Doubtless our forebears failed to realize, however, if they thought about the matter at all, that the turbine has far greater efficiency—that is to say, gets far more work out of a given quantity of water—than the other wheels.

MORSE TELEGRAPH INSTRUMENT

The modern mechanic knows this, and he has learned to construct a turbine so skilfully that it can transform more than 90 per cent of the energy of falling water into the energy of rotary motion of an axle. More than that, he has learned how to fasten on the axle what is called the rotor of a dynamo, and thus to transform the energy of rotary motion into the energy of electricity. For a good many years now he has been doing this on an increasingly imposing scale, and the culmination — for the moment — was reached when a generator of this type was set in motion at Niagara Falls that uses 3,200 cubic feet of water per second and develops 70,000 horsepower.

NIAGARA POWER PLANT

Letting Water Do the Work

THIS power plant on the Puyallup River, at Electron, near Tacoma, Washington, utilizes a drop of 865 feet. The force that gravity gives to water falling such a distance is well illustrated by the cannon-like discharge of the streams as they issue from the pipe-line by-pass valves when temporarily off their job.

The Mercury-Vapor Engine

IT is not in the least surprizing to learn that the inventor of the mercury-vapor engine, Dr. William Leroy Emmet, of the General Electric Company, was engaged for ten years on the project that now finds practical realization; for the difficulties involved in making the vapor of a liquid that boils at minimum temperature of 677 degrees Fahrenheit do the work of steam must be enormous. Yet it is interesting to reflect that the principles utilized in the new and highly ingenious invention are all perfectly familiar to physicists and mechanical engineers.

The essential principle that accounts for steam engine and gas engine and mercury-vapor engine alike is that vapors and gases tend to expand when heated. The higher the temperature, the greater the force of expansion—hence the power of superheated steam, and, to make the present application, of mercury vapor. Water under normal conditions

POWER PLANT IN WASHINGTON

changes into vapor that thrusts in every direction with relatively tremendous power when brought to a temperature of 212 degrees Fahrenheit. Mercury remains a liquid, with expansive power dormant, until brought to a temperature 465 degrees higher, but the power of expansion of the vapor that then results is proportionately greater than that of ordinary steam.

Dr. Emmet's engine provides a boiler of very special construction, with welded joints, in which mercury is brought to the boiling point. The mercury vapor, expanding with terrific force, drives a turbine of familiar type, which is, in effect, a highly specialized windmill. To the shaft of this mercury-vapor turbine the rotor of an electric generator is attached, just as in case of an ordinary steam turbine.

But the mercury vapor after coming through the turbine is still excessively hot, and the water that is introduced to cool it is turned into steam at high pressure, which is used to operate a steam turbine—giving power, of course, for another generator. And the mercury vapor, having given up its heat to the water, is condensed and runs back to the original boiler as liquid mercury. A given quantity of mercury, amounting to only five pounds for each kilowatt of power generated, is thus used over and over, there being no chance for it to escape from the closed system through which it circulates.

There are sundry highly important practical details of operation, such as the use of the fuel gases for four distinct purposes before they escape up the chimney; and the net result, it is claimed, is a saving of 40 to 50 per cent of the fuel requisite to generate a given quantity of electricity with steam engines hitherto regarded as relatively efficient.

Courtesy of the General Electric Co
THE MERCURY-VAPOR ENGINE

How Genius Rang a Bell

JOSEPH HENRY, who died in 1878, did many things that are of interest to radio users, because his chief scientific activities had to do with electromagnetism, in the study of which he was a pioneer; and he did at least two things that are readily comprehensible to all of us as eminently useful achievements—he made electromagnets that would lift more than a ton, and he rang a bell from a distance by electricity. The last-named feat in particular has been stressed in recent articles, and a picture showing the original electromagnet and the first bell to be thus sounded has been widely published.

Now the ringing of a bell at a distance by electricity is one of the most familiar every-day occurrences—as the telephone bell and push-button call-bell incessantly remind us. But there were no such devices as these in the world in 1831, when Joseph Henry made his classic experiment of ringing the little bell by impact of the armature

QUEBEC BRIDGE

A Monument to a Century of Peace

THE Buffalo-Fort Erie Peace Bridge commemorating one hundred years of peace between Canada and the United States is an architectural structure of interest and importance. But this aspect of the bridge is insignificant in comparison with its status as a souvenir of what perhaps is a unique historical record—the maintenance of absolute peace between two contiguous nations for a full century. Such a record makes one dare to hope that Man, the great predator and the most belligerent of animals, is progressing toward civilization. Incidentally, the bridge has a length of 4,200 feet, and a capacity of 3,000 automobiles per hour. During the first year of its operation (it opened June 1, 1927), it was used by between five and six million people.

The other photographs show the international bridge at Niagara and the bridge over the St. Lawrence at Quebec.

Science Safeguards Miners

WHEN a cartridge of dynamite is thrust into a drill hole it may become lodged there and require to be rammed down, as a bullet is rammed into an old-fashioned muzzle-loading gun. If too much friction is developed, the cartridge ignites, and then comes disaster. The Bureau of Mines experts have invented a machine that tells how much friction each explosive will stand, and its results are now available to all miners.

INTERNATIONAL BRIDGE AT NIAGARA

of an electromagnet of a new type that he had just devised.

Furthermore, no one prior to that memorable day had been able to make an electromagnet thus operate in response to an electric current generated at a distance. The electromagnet itself had been invented only a few years before by an Englishman, William Sturgeon, but the type of apparatus he had devised would operate only when placed near the electric source.

Joseph Henry's genius led him to create a new type of electromagnet by using many turns of wire insulated with a silk covering, and to connect this with a number of batteries in series; and the so-called "intensive" system thus evolved proved revolutionary, in that it permitted the operation of the electromagnet over a long stretch of wire, and thus, among other things, laid the foundation for the electric telegraph that came into practical use a few years later.

Every electric bell gives tribute to the genius of America's greatest physicist; and the name of the man himself is often on the lips of the radio expert, when he computes the power of his induction coils in "henrys" or "microhenrys." Yet the average user of radio-receivers probably gives no more thought to the origin of these words than the telephone user gives to the origin of the call-bell.

BUFFALO-FORT ERIE PEACE BRIDGE

The Sault Ste. Marie Bascule Bridge

BUILT by the Canadian Pacific Railroad Co. at Sault Ste. Marie, Michigan, each "bascule" leaf weighs about 400 tons. Total length of bridge, 356 feet. It is operated electrically, and the bascule leaves can be opened and closed in one and one-quarter minutes.

ANOTHER VIEW OF THE BASCULE BRIDGE

THE SAULT STE. MARIE BASCULE BRIDGE

The Hudson River Bridge at Bear Mountain

THIS unusually long suspension bridge, with its concrete highway approaches, is an outstanding marvel of mechanical engineering. To the thoughtful motorist who is not a trained engineer, the crossing of this bridge (and others of its kind) seems a veritable Aladdin's journey. Even with the bridge in being, it seems incredible that human ingenuity could forecast such a project, and carry it to successful completion.

To Bore a Square Hole

THE more one thinks about it the clearer it becomes that the only kind of hole that could be bored with a revolving instrument of any kind would be a round hole.

Now, roundness is an excellent quality in a hole if perchance you wish to fit into it a round peg. But what if it would serve your purpose better to use a square peg or one that is oval or triangular? Then it certainly would be convenient to be able to bore a hole that is not round. But can the thing be done?

Until somewhat recently every carpenter would have answered that question with an emphatic negative.

He would have told you that if you want to make a hole that is square, for example, you must first bore a round hole and then gouge out the corners with that very primitive tool, the chisel.

But these are days when the impossible is perpetually happening. And so along comes Mr. C. H. Schmidgall, of Peoria, Ill., to show us that it is quite feasible to bore square holes or triangular ones, or for that matter holes that are star-shaped or octagonal or in the form of a Maltese cross or what not.

This is not accomplished by the waving of a magic wand, however. Fourteen years of experiment and effort were required to perfect the machine that does the trick.

Yet the principle employed is almost embarrassingly simple—embarrassing, I mean, for the skeptics who said the thing could not be done.

The basic principle is merely to adjust lateral boring devices, like auger ends of various shapes, to the same matrix that carries the ordinary auger.

The latter bores a round hole in advance; and the auxiliary augers, operating at right angles to the other, bore out the angles. A familiar type of "worm" gearing on the central shaft actuates all the augers simultaneously.

So one more mechanical problem is solved, and the world's work facilitated for the benefit of all of us.

BEAR MOUNTAIN BRIDGE

Before the Horse Was Displaced

THE combination harvester, pulled by thirty-odd horses (count 'em for yourself) was a marvel of the late nineteenth century. Now the tractor, gasoline driven, has largely superseded the horse in large-scale farming operations. Times change so rapidly that even now the horse-pulled apparatus seems more astonishing than its motored successor.

BEFORE THE HORSE WAS DISPLACED

Photograph by Underwood and Underwood

Mechanical Hen That Lays Eggs

A MARVEL of ingenuity is this laboratory in the form of a hen, which performs mechanically a series of intricate chemical and physical manipulations through which the raw material going into the composition of an egg and its shell is made under electrical power. It involves no really new principle, but gives a thought-provocative demonstration of several old ones.

Setting Type by the Line

LARGE-SCALE typesetting nowadays is mostly done with the famous linotype machine, which is operated by striking keys like those of a typewriter. The "typesetter" thus has nothing to do directly with type. In fact, type is not used at all as individual units. At the end of each line, the operator touches a button, which causes the type-molds to be fixed; and type-metal is automatically poured into the mold, to form a slug one line in length. These slugs, as the metal cools, are automatically piled in sequence, and can be removed and locked together for direct printing or for the making of electrotype or other plates. Any error made by the operator can be corrected only by the production of a substitute line. If the operator makes few mistakes, the cost of typesetting is minimized, and there is great saving of time and labor, as compared with hand-setting.

SETTING TYPE BY THE LINE

Milking by Electricity

OF course the electricity merely supplies the suction-power by operating the air-compressing mechanism. But the method would hardly be introduced on a large scale without the convenience of electrical distribution of power. In any case, the mechanical milker is a boon that every farm-reared man who remembers his boyhood will be disposed to rank high among beneficent inventions—not merely as a labor-saver, but a temper-saver of the first order. For the old-time method of "extracting the lacteal" was a task that tried the very soul of youth, and probably held first rank among provocatives of profanity.

Counting Atoms

WHEN men of science talk about atoms nowadays, they are likely to reel off sets of figures that might lead one to infer that an atom is of not much more consequence than a German mark. For example, we are told that the number of atoms in a cubic centimeter of helium gas is 2,560,000,000,000,000,000,000.

That absurd row of figures might be read, I believe, two sextillion, five hundred and sixty quintillion. Quadrillions and trillions and paltry millions, it will be observed, are thrown off in round numbers—a sort of "keep the change" effect.

Whether or not we name them, such rows of figures of course mean nothing at all to most of us. Our minds balk at the attempt to visualize anything much beyond thousands. Perhaps it will help a little if we make a calculation showing that if the atoms of helium gas in a little glass pellet the size of a pea were to be liberated at the rate of one thousand per second, about two thousand million years would elapse before the last atom escaped.

But how does anyone know that such figures represent anything but sheer imagining? That, after all, is the question of real interest. One would like to know why the man of science fixed on one row of figures rather than another.

And now comes the surprize. When we seek to ascertain just how the atom-counting is done we find that the process is quite simple. The principle involved is not different from that used by a farmer who wishes to count the sheep in a large flock.

The method consists in making a small hole, accurately measured, in a screen against which so-called "alpha particles," which are really helium atoms, are bombarded from a measured surface of radium.

MODERN MILKING WITH ELECTRIC POWER

THE MACHINE THAT SUPPLIES THE POWER FOR MILKING

The particles are flying impartially in all directions, so those that go through the hole—one by one, like sheep—are a calculable fraction of the whole number given off in a given time.

Echoes from the Sea Bottom

A SPECIALLY devised radio-receiving apparatus on a ship has been able to detect and amplify to audibility the infinitely minute waves of sound sent down from the ship to the sea bottom, and reflected thence to the surface precisely as an echo comes back through the air from a mountainside.

When it is recorded that the sound-signal sent down into the water from the ship may pass to a depth of two or three miles before reaching the sea bottom from which it is echoed back, the delicacy of the instrument that can detect the echo will be appreciated.

A CLOSE-UP OF THE AUTOMATIC MILKER

SPERRY GYROSCOPE ON S. S. *PRESIDENT WILSON*

The Stabilizing Gyroscope

THE spinning top is so familiar a toy that you probably have never thought of its action as extraordinary. Yet if the same top, when not spinning, were to stand erect, in defiance of gravitation, you would think the phenomenon altogether astonishing.

If you seek an explanation of the anomaly, now that your attention is called to it, you will be told that the spinning top owes its stability to gyroscopic action. You will be further informed, perhaps, that every whirling body, from the smallest top to our big earth itself, is a gyroscope; and that every gyroscope, whatever its size, tends to retain a fixed position while spinning.

It is gyroscopic action, for example, that keeps the earth's axis aimed at the Pole Star, insuring us a regular succession of seasons. The boy's top takes on new interest when we reflect that the principle of action that holds it erect is the same principle that determines beyond peradventure the coming of the summer solstice in June and of the winter solstice in December.

Naming a principle does not necessarily explain it. But let it suffice for the moment that "gyroscopic action" does stabilize the whirling body, and that practical use may be made of the principle in a number of interesting ways.

It is possible, for example, to adjust a small perpetually spinning gyroscope so that its axis, pointing always to the pole, will serve as a non-magnetic compass. Modern ships are equipped with such compasses, the invention of the late Elmer E. Sperry.

Another Sperry success in this field is in the form of a gigantic gyroscopic apparatus for stabilizing ships at sea. It is a mammoth top to be adjusted in the hold of a ship. Kept spinning by mechanical power, it will tend to hold rigidly the upright position, and thus check the rolling motion of the ship.

The ship stabilizer must be of ponderous size, because it must have power to push significantly against the weight of the rolling ship itself. The apparatus exhibited by Mr. Sperry weighs 120

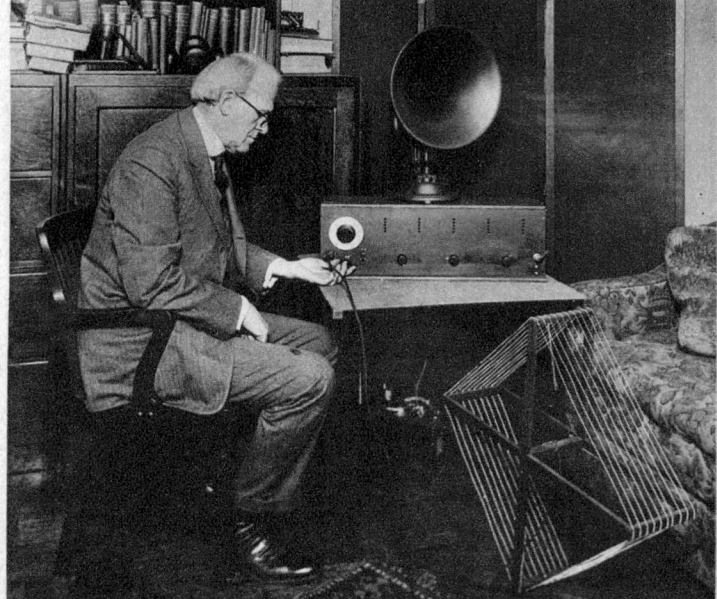

AN EARLY EXPERIMENTER WITH THE DIRECTIONAL LOOP-AERIAL

tons. Even that seems a small affair in comparison with a modern ship; but the gyroscope acts instantaneously, and thus tends to check the ship's roll before it attains irresistible momentum.

Radio on the Lightship

LIFE on a lightship is usually regarded as a synonym for loneliness and isolation.

The very fact that the lightship is located not far from land seems to make the isolation all the greater.

In no other location, perhaps, is radio calculated to perform a larger service.

Doubtless the greatest specific service that radio will be called upon to render habitually in this location will be the cooperation with land stations in giving ships their bearings in time of fog or storm.

THE LATEST STEAMLESS STEAMSHIP

The part of the radio apparatus that makes this possible is the so-called radio compass, which is essentially a loop-aerial used in connection with an ordinary compass.

The loop-aerial, as is well known, is highly directional. By rotating it, one determines at once the direction from which a radio message comes.

Edgewise, the message is loud; broadside, it fades. A single observation may reveal that a ship sending the message is too near in shore, and a warning return message may serve to avert disaster.

Radio for the Befogged Ship

AMONG notable achievements is the perfection of methods for the utilization of the radio compass to enable ships befogged at sea to get their bearings.

The ship is equipped with a "radio compass," which is merely a loop-aerial adjusted in connection with an ordinary compass, and can therefore determine the exact direction of the lighthouse from which a

FOG SIGNALS ON FIRE ISLAND LIGHTSHIP

LATEST RADIO IN FIRE ISLAND LIGHTSHIP

signal is received. By charting the direction of two signals from different stations, the point of intersection reveals the location of the ship.

It is, of course, necessary to distinguish a signal as coming from a particular lighthouse of known location, else the charting obviously could not be done. This is made possible by an ingenious system of automatic timing, according to which each lighthouse sends out signals at given intervals.

An earlier method of using the radio compass required the signals to be sent from the ship to be intercepted by land stations provided with radio compasses. Two land stations, each noting the direction of a signaling ship, compared notes, as it were, by telephone, or sent their records to a central station, where the comparison was made. The direction lines being charted at this central land station, the location of the ship would be thus revealed, and the finding would be radioed to the navigator.

When this system is used, we have the interesting paradox of a befogged navigator, perhaps two or three hundred miles at sea, receiving notification from land as to just where he is. In effect the skilled navigator on the ship signals by radio, "Please tell me where I am, for I have not seen the sky for hours and am sailing by dead reckoning"; and the landlubber, who perhaps knows nothing at all about navigation, signals back: "You are at forty degrees and thirty minutes north latitude and seventy-two degrees and forty minutes west longitude" (or abbreviations to that effect), and the navigator knows that he is just where he should be, off the coast of Long Island.

The newer system, as above described, is less paradoxical, permitting the navigator on the ship to determine his own position, aided only by automatic signals; but in each case the effective instrument is the direction-finding loop-aerial that constitutes the brains—or should we say the eyes and ears?—of the radio-compass.

A Spinning Top at the Helm

GYROSCOPES have been so nearly perfected that airplanes without living pilots have risen into the air, made long flights, and come safely to earth, controlled solely by the big top at the helm.

A GYROSCOPE-BALANCED CAR

Historic World Flights

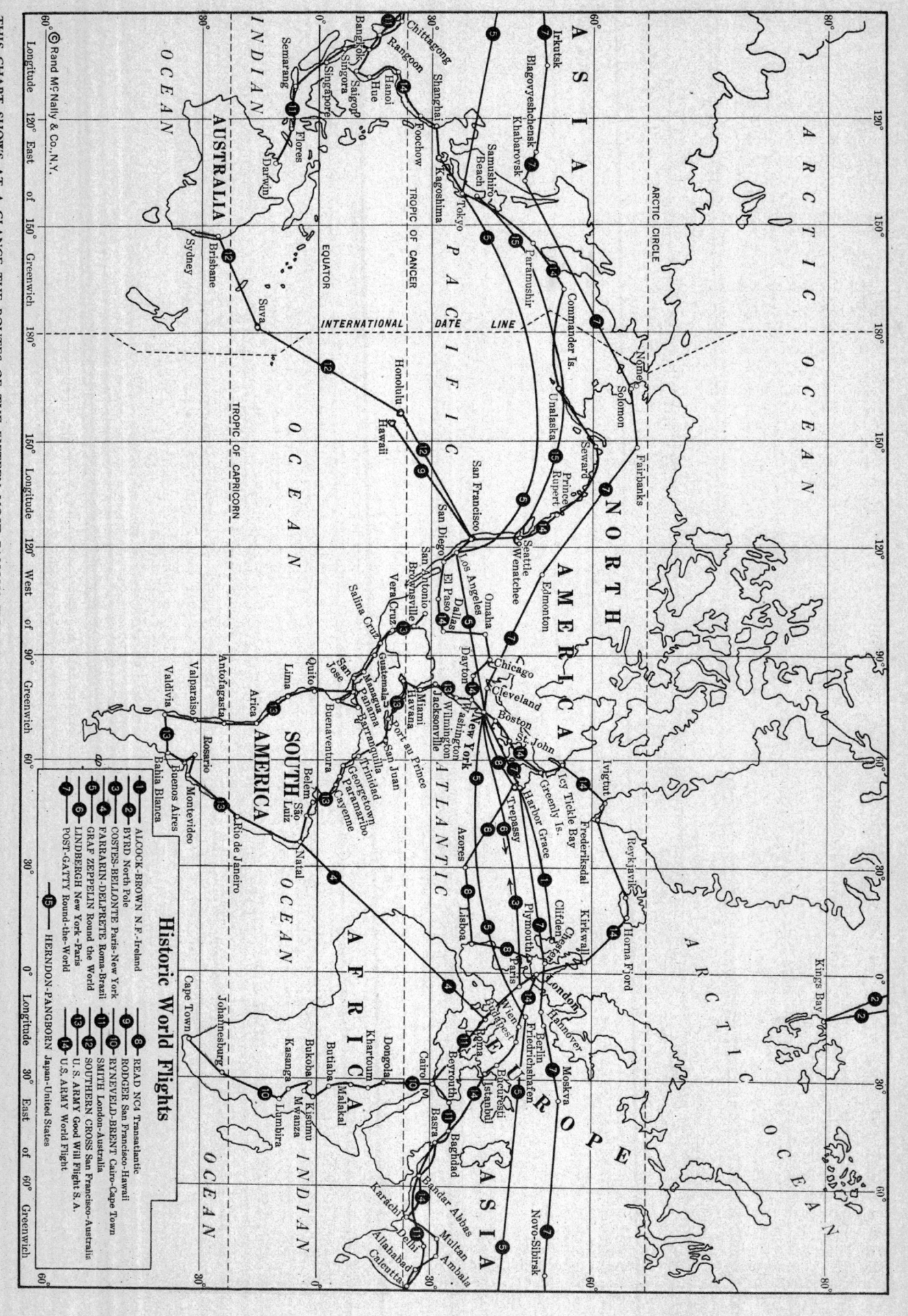

1. ALCOCK-BROWN N.F.-Ireland
2. BYRD North Pole
3. COSTES-BELLONTE Paris-New York
4. FARRARIN-DELPRETE Roma-Brazil
5. GRAF ZEPPELIN Round the World
6. LINDBERGH New York-Paris
7. POST-GATTY Round-the-World
8. READ NC4 Transatlantic
9. RODGER San Francisco-Hawaii
10. RYNEVELD-BRENT Cairo-Cape Town
11. SMITH London-Australia
12. SOUTHERN CROSS San Francisco-Australia
13. U.S. ARMY Good Will Flight S. A.
14. U.S. ARMY World Flight
15. HERNDON-PANGBORN Japan-United States

THIS CHART SHOWS AT A GLANCE THE ROUTES OF THE FIFTEEN MOST FAMOUS FLIGHTS BY AIRPLANE OR DIRIGIBLE, FROM THE FIRST TRANSATLANTIC HOP BY ALCOCK AND BROWN TO THE HISTORIC NON-STOP FLIGHT OVER THE PACIFIC BY HERNDON AND PANGBORN. FIVE OF THE FIFTEEN HAVE CROSSED THE MYSTERIOUS INTERNATIONAL DATE LINE, SHOWN ON CHART, WHERE YOU SUDDENLY LOSE A WHOLE DAY WHEN GOING WEST, OR GAIN A WHOLE DAY WHEN COMING EAST

© Rand McNally & Co., N.Y.